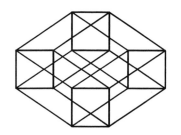

Hypercube, Inc.

Laboratory Exercises Using HyperChem®

Mary L. Caffery

Clarke College, Dubuque, IA

Paul A. Dobosh

Mount Holyoke College, South Hadley, MA

Diane M. Richardson

Molecular Applications Group, Palo Alto, CA

May 1998

Copyright © 1998 Hypercube, Inc.

ISBN 1-896164-30-7

Hypercube Trademarks

ChemPlus, HyperChem Data, and HyperChem Raytrace are trademarks of Hypercube, Inc. HyperChem, HyperChem Lite, HyperMM+, HyperNewton, HyperEHT, HyperNDO, HyperGauss, and HyperNMR are trademarks of Hypercube, Inc.

Third Party Trademarks

Microsoft, MS-DOS, and Excel are registered trademarks, and Windows, Windows NT, and Windows 95 are trademarks of Microsoft Corporation. All other brand and product names are trademarks or registered trademarks of their respective holders.

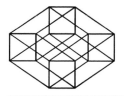

Table of Contents

Chapter 9. Teaching Notes and Results.......................... 205

Foreword

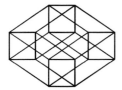

Some thoughts on including molecular modeling across the chemistry curriculum.

Most undergraduates enrolling in chemistry classes today are reasonably "computer literate." They come with basic skills such as word processing, searching the World Wide Web and to a lesser extent, using spreadsheets for calculations. They are accustomed to high quality graphics and have a facility for interpreting three-dimensional scenes from the numerous "games" they have played. Their learning styles have been changed – it is no longer text-based.

While some disciplines will need to search for meaningful ways to address the learning style of today's students, we chemists have the advantage of a powerful tool that not only has educational value, it also has made a substantial impact on how chemistry is done in the workplace. The advent of high quality programs that run on PCs has made molecular modeling a tool that can be incorporated at any level in the chemistry curriculum relatively inexpensively.

My philosophy in developing these exercises is that use of molecular modeling tools should be as pervasive in the undergraduate chemistry curriculum as a simple spectrophotometer or pH meter. Indeed, it can be done at considerably less expense! I do have some concerns related to the curriculum development. They are presented in no particular priority.

- While students at earlier developmental stages need experiments that give relatively good results, all students should be aware that models are just that - models, not reality. The experiments described here are based on sophisticated calculations that can be done on a PC in a relatively short time. Sometimes accuracy has been sacrificed in the suggested setup to save time. Time matters… no one is very patient in front of a computer!

- Images don't come with built-in instructions on how they should be read. Students may not "see" the same thing that a faculty member does. They need assistance in interpreting different renderings of molecules, molecular orbitals, and various surfaces.

- Connections should be made between theoretical modeling work and experimental variables from the lab. The relation between experimental work and what can be reliably computed needs to be discussed. Some lessons should complement actual experiments that undergraduates perform. Computer modeling must never replace the laboratory experimentation.

- Lessons should enhance critical thinking. A working definition I use is adapted from the home page of the Critical Thinking Community [http://www.sonoma.edu/cthink/]: "thinking that generates, organizes, analyzes, synthesizes, evaluates and transforms content." My students usually need a good deal of experience in learning how to organize and to transform content by presenting information graphically as well as in words.

- A variety of teaching methods should used: small-group learning, cooperative learning, project-centered classes, individual assignments. Molecular modeling gives instructors a powerful tool for enhancing collaboration among students. More "what if?" questions can result from an increasing amount of data as students pool work on slightly different systems and compare their results.

The possibilities for academic use of molecular modeling are endless and the purpose of this book is to provide a source for faculty looking for a starting point for developing exercises. The exercises presented here are not ideally arranged for a two or three hour lab and may contain more or less than an instructor desires. The plan was not to present perfectly encapsulated exercises but instead to present a lot of interesting information that instructors can modify as they wish.

I wish to express sincere thanks to Clarke College, Dubuque, Iowa for two enriching sabbaticals during which I first learned the basics of molecular modeling and then had the time to complete the current work. Some of the exercises presented here were developed as part of a NSF-CCD project (DUE: 9354515) at Clarke College. That financial support is gratefully acknowledged.

Paul A. Dobosh and Diane M. Richardson express thanks to the Pew Foundation and Mount Holyoke College for early support in developing some of these exercises as part of the Pew NECUSE grant program to a consortium of New England colleges and universities.

MLC

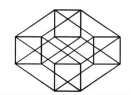

Chapter 1
Building and Visualizing Molecules

"When it comes to atoms, language can be used only as in poetry. The poet too, is not so nearly concerned with describing facts as with creating images." - Neils Bohr

A distinctive feature of HyperChem, the "new instrument" introduced here, is the Model Builder that allows one to simply sketch two-dimensional representations of molecules and convert them into three-dimensional structures with the click of a button. The two dimensional structures can be drawn directly using HyperChem or imported from drawing programs such as MDL Information Systems ISIS/Draw or ChemDraw.

The transformation process is based on a set of rules about valency and structure that is built into HyperChem. This first chapter of exercises is to encourage a back and forth learning process whereby a student determines both the power and limitations of the Model Builder. HyperChem also includes several tools that can be used to get correct conformations or chirality for more complicated structures. The use of amino acid and nucleic acid databases will also be introduced.

While the screen-images we generate with HyperChem might be perfectly understandable to the teacher who sees them filtered through a rich background in chemistry, the beginning student needs some instruction on how an image should be interpreted. Exercise 2 explores some of the visualization tools in HyperChem including both two-dimensional contour maps and three-dimensional isosurfaces. The remaining exercises illustrate specific tools that can aid in modeling more complex molecules.

1. Building Small Molecules

HyperChem has a sophisticated model building algorithm that starts with the connectivity in a molecule, along with some information about multiple bonds, and constructs a 3-dimensional molecule. The modelbuilder works quite well with organic molecules, with the occasional odd problem. It will be useful to get a sense of what it can do with a range of inorganic compounds. In the first exercise, we'll examine several groups of molecules to see how the modelbuilder squares with our knowledge of molecules, their shapes, atomic valance and so on.

Build the following diatomic molecules. Be certain that both Explicit Hydrogens and Allow Ions are NOT checked in the Build menu. Use a stick rendering. Construct each diatomic with a single bond between the atoms. Have the modelbuilder construct the molecules by double clicking on the select cursor or by moving down to Add H and Model Build in the build menu. Note the shape of the molecule and if the model builder added any hydrogen. Then determine what molecule you've built. Finally, view the molecule in some space-filling rendering to get a sense of the size of the molecule. You can construct several molecules on the same screen to see relative sizes.

Repeat the process of constructing the diatomic molecule but this time, L-click on the bond between the two atoms to increase the bond to a double bond. How does HyperChem respond and why?

Repeat one last time and increase the bond order to a triple bond with two separate clicks. If the clicks are too closely spaced a dashed line will be drawn indicating a half bond increase. This is useful for modeling delocalization but is not wanted here. You can R-click on a bond to decrease its bond order.

Molecule	Single Bond	Double Bond	Triple bond
H_2			
N_2			
O_2			
C_2			
F_2			

Oxoacids

Construct the following non-ionized forms of some oxoacids. Pay attention to both size and shape. Include double bonds as needed. Use the rotation tools to examine the three-dimensional nature of the molecules.

H_2CO_3	H_3BO_3	H_2SO_4	H_2SO_3
HNO_3	HNO_2	H_4GeO_4	H_3PO_4
$HClO_4$	$HClO_3$	$HClO_2$	$HClO$

Oxygen Allotropes

The allotropic forms of oxygen are diatomic oxygen and triatomic ozone. Build O_2 with a double bond and invoke the modelbuilder. Use the select tool to L-click on the bond and note the bond length on the status line. How does it compare with the experimental value of 1.208Å?

Check Allow Ions on the Build menu. Now build ozone using two different methods. In one case, join the three oxygens using one double and one single bond. Modelbuild and observe what happens. Measure the distances and angles. Is this a correct structure? Next, build a delocalized form. After connecting the oxygens with single bonds rapidly double click each bond. You should see a dotted lined indicating a partial bond order. Modelbuild and again measure the distances and angles.

Carbon Allotropes

Carbon has three well-known allotropes: graphite, diamond and buckminsterfullerene. Build a 35-40-atom fragment of the first two allotropes. Compare these with HyperChem's pre-built buckminsterfullerene (Hyper5/Aromatic/c60.hin)

Graphite has a layered structure in which each layer consists of planar, hexagonal aromatic rings of carbon atoms that are fused together in a continuous network. This can be drawn easily starting with the three-ring system such as anthracene (Hyper5/Aromatic/anthracene.hin), converting each of the hydrogens to carbon and connecting the new carbon atoms in six-member rings. Double click the added bonds to produce the resonance structure and then modelbuild.

Building the diamond fragment can be a challenge for the modelbuilder. Here is one way of proceeding. Construct $C(CH_3)_4$ using the draw cursor with carbon as the chosen element. Convert each H to a C by clicking on it with the cursor. Then Add H and Model Build again.

Find pairs of hydrogen atoms that are almost overlapping and convert each pair of hydrogen to a single carbon. Do this by deleting one hydrogen (R-click) and then drawing a bond from the carbon that held the deleted hydrogen to the other hydrogen, converting it to carbon.

Click on any remaining hydrogen pointing into space to convert them to carbons. Check Explicit Hydrogens and then invoke the Add Hydrogens command but **do not** modelbuild. Once more, convert strongly interacting pairs of hydrogen to a single carbon atom but leave the "exo" hydrogens alone. Once again, Add Hydrogens.

Next, carry out a MM+ geometry optimization. If you notice any interacting pairs of hydrogen during this process, cancel the optimization; convert them to a C and Add Hydrogen. Eventually you will have eliminated any strain from hydrogen atoms bumping into each other and the system will reach a symmetric minimum, a hydrogenated diamond fragment.

If you have sufficient memory in your computer, try an Extended Hückel calculation on the three allotropic forms. Look at the orbital energy diagrams, noting the filled and unfilled orbitals. Measure the energy gap between LUMO and HOMO for each. Can you relate this to your knowledge of the band structure conductivity properties of each form?

2. Visualizing Structure and Charge Distribution

HyperChem allows one to visualize the geometric arrangements of atoms using a variety of structural models. Each rendering technique carries different information that will be explored in the first part.

Another important aspect of visualization is the use of two-dimensional and three-dimensional maps to explore certain electronic properties. This will be explored in the second part.

Molecular Rendering

Use a small molecule such as acetic acid or carbonic acid to observe each of the following rendering methods. Note the advantages and drawbacks of each. After each rendering, use the out-of plane rotation tool to rotate the molecule to get a good sense of its 3-dimensional structure.

Acetic Acid   Carbonic Acid

Sticks

In a stick model representation, a colored line represents each bond, but the atoms located at the endpoints are not explicitly drawn. Double, triple and partial bonds are visible if "Show Multiple Bonds" is checked on the display menu. The element colors carry no additional meaning and can be changed by the user. It is a good idea to use default colors initially.

Wedges can be used to show perspective. Choose Rendering on the display menu. Use Sticks and in the Sticks property box choose Wedges, then L-click OK. L-click on the drawing tool and place it over one of the carbon-hydrogen bonds. Hold down the shift key and L-click. Solid wedges mean, "bond up" (out of screen); dashed wedges mean, "bond down" (behind the screen). L-click on a carbon-hydrogen bond on the other carbon. Use the out of plane rotate tool to rotate the molecule and see how it changes.

You may want to check Show Inertial Axes on the Display menu to see how the molecular axes are drawn. The primary inertial axis (#1) is the longest distance through the molecule. The tertiary axis (#3) is the shortest.

Balls

The van der Waals surface of an atom is related to the radii of non-bonded atoms held together only by weak intermolecular forces. A surface at that radius would enclose about 90-95% of the electrons. When Balls is selected a colored sphere of van der Waals radius represents each atom of the molecule. They are drawn from back to front and are not shown as overlapping.

Balls and Cylinders

The molecule is represented with small spheres defining the atoms and with cylinders for the bonds. The size of the ball is proportional to the van der Waals radius. Single, double and triple bonds are not shown.

Overlapping Spheres

This rendering shows each atom of the molecule using a colored sphere of van der Waals radius. The atoms are drawn overlapping.

Dots

This renders a transparent, space-filling model with the van der Waals surface shown in dots.

Sticks and Dots

This is a combination of the transparent van der Waals surface and the stick representation.

Electron Charge Distribution

HyperChem includes a number of semi-empirical calculation methods that will allow us to visualize the probability of finding the electrons in a molecule (i.e. the electron density or charge density). We will begin with relatively simple diatomic molecules to explore how the electron density can be visualized using HyperChem.

Build diatomic hydrogen. Invoke the modelbuilder. This should align the molecular axis on the y-axis

Use the Setup menu to select an Extended Hückel calculation. The options should show a charge of zero and multiplicity of 1. Do not change the other selections. Do a single point calculation from the Compute menu. After it is complete, choose Plot Molecular Properties from the compute menu. Check Total Charge Density and 2D contours. Then click on Contour Grid tab and use the settings shown in the figures below.

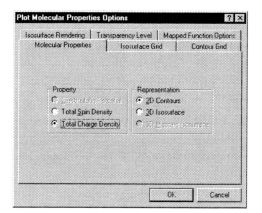 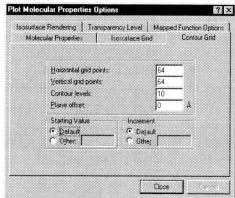

This should produce a 2-D contour diagram like the one shown below. The contour lines represent the electron density in the molecule if you sliced through the plane of the molecule containing the bond. The unit of electron density is e/a_o^3 where e is the unit of charge and a_o is the Bohr radius (0.529 Å).

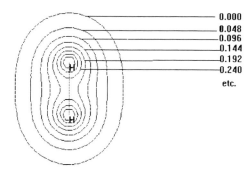

The grid represents an array of points in the plane of the molecule (the screen plane) where the calculation of electron density will be done.

The higher the number of grid points the longer the calculation will be! The 64 x 64 grid is a convenient choice for this exercise.

HyperChem computes the maximum and minimum values of electron density on the grid and then draws contour lines evenly spaced in between the maximum and minimum values. In this case notice that the default starting value is very near zero and the increment is approximately 0.048. The diagram shows how the electron density changes as you get closer to the nuclei. Notice that the lines get closer as you move toward the nuclei but that there is a symmetric electron distribution in H_2. Depending on the settings for the number of contour lines, initial value, and increment, you may not see all of the contour lines. It is good to use the default settings until you understand how the settings change the appearance of the diagram.

What would happen if we sliced through the electron cloud and looked at it above or below the plane containing the nuclei, i.e. $\pm z$? We can do this by changing the Offset value. Positive values slice the electron cloud above the plane; negative values slice it below the plane. Select Plot Molecular Properties and the Contour Grid properties box. Use an offset of 0.3. What happens? Can you explain why the image looks different?

Hydrogen Fluoride

Draw and model build hydrogen fluoride, HF. Use the default settings to show the contour lines. Observe that the electron density is now pulled toward the electronegative fluorine atom.

You can save the image for later printing by using Edit menu-Copy Image. This copies the workspace to the clipboard from which it can be pasted into a document for printing. First, on the File-Preferences menu select Setup Image. Check the Workspace box under Windows, Bitmap under File Format and the Clipboard as the destination. You will probably also want to set the screen background color to white. Do this from the File-Preferences-Window Color menu.

Finally, draw and model build LiH. Use the default settings to show the contour lines. What happens in this case?

Compare the bonding in H_2, HF and LiH. Which one seems to be primarily "ionic", that is, the electron density is located on one atom?

Spin Density

Nitrogen oxide, NO, is a neutral molecule with one unpaired electron. While it was the nitrogen atom that brought an odd number of electrons to the system, it is of interest to see where the unpaired spin resides in the molecule. Draw and modelbuild NO.

Under the Setup menu, check Semi-empirical and Extended Hückel. Use the Options box to set the spin multiplicity to 2 leaving the charge of zero as shown. Do the single point calculation. Then under Plot Molecular properties, choose Total Spin Density and 2-D contours using the default settings.

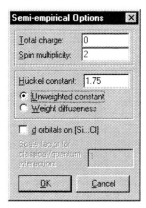

Where does the unpaired electron reside?

You can do 3-D contour surfaces of the spin density in the same manner as you did charge density.

Isosurfaces

One thing you have probably noticed is that if you rotate the molecule, the contour diagram disappears. This is because the calculation of contours is no longer valid since x, y and z have changed. Selecting an isosurface plot is equivalent to selecting one of the contour lines. An isosurface is the surface in space where the electron density has the same value. This surface can be rotated in 3-D space. The surface at 0.002 encloses about 98% of the electron density in the molecule. Remember that if you use a larger number, you are moving closer to the nuclei. The figure of HF at the right was produced using the settings shown below.

The isosurface grid was set to medium and on the isosurface-rendering tab, the contour value was 0.002 and translucent shading was used. The molecular rendering was done in the usual manner using spheres to show the van der Waal surface relative to the electron density.

Try several different settings of the charge density contour value to see how the image changes. What would you expect the 0.240 isosurface of hydrogen to look like? This is done using the Plot Molecular Properties Options as shown on the next page.

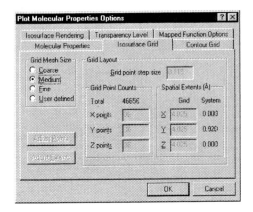 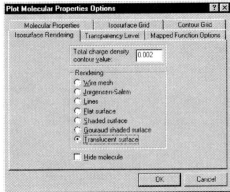

Electrostatic Potential

Electrostatic potential is defined as the potential energy that an external point charge (i.e. a proton) would experience in the presence of the molecule. The calculation includes contributions of both the nuclei and the electrons and therefore represents a good model to predict where reactions might occur.

Two- and three-dimensional contour maps can be made as previously shown. Notice here, color is used to indicate a positive or negative potential. The default colors are green for positive and violet for negative. These can be changed in the File-Preferences dialog box.

For this exercise, draw and model build ammonia, NH_3. It is not necessary to include the lone pair in the drawing. Use CNDO to do a geometry optimization. Select Plot Molecular Properties from the Compute menu and use the following settings on the indicated menu tabs.

Molecular Properties:	Electrostatic Potential
	3D Isosurface
Isosurface Grid:	Medium
Isosurface rendering:	Contour value 0.09
	Gouraud shaded surface

Rotate the molecule. Note the negative potential violet "lobe" in the vicinity of the lone pair. This indicates a site of attraction for an external positive charge. The region of repulsion (positive potential) is shown in green.

A **3D-mapped** isosurface can give you a better sense of how large these attractive or repulsive electrostatic potentials are. From the Compute-Plot Molecular properties menu select

Electrostatic Potential   3D-Mapped Isosurface OK

Under Mapped Function Options, be sure that the Display range legend is checked. HyperChem will choose appropriate maximum and minimum values for the display. Check OK.

When the plot is made the gradations in color are indicative of the variation in charge density as indicated on the map. Also note on the status line the actual maximum and minimum electrostatic potentials are displayed. For ammonia the minimum is -0.188 and the maximum is $+0.526$. Try resetting the mapped function options to ± 0.188 to see how the display changes.

Draw each of the hydrogen halides, HX where X = F, Cl, Br, I. Use AM1 to obtain an optimized geometry. Plot the 3D electrostatic potential map at a contour level of 0.002, which is about equivalent to the 98% envelope. You may notice that in some cases you get a very large maximum value. This is an artifact of the calculation and is related to the grid. If a nucleus is coincidentally positioned at one of the grid points a large repulsion occurs.

3. Stereoisomers: Carvone and Hexahellicene

Many of the molecules we need to construct for calculations can be built with a few mouse clicks and use of the modelbuilder function. Occasionally, the modeler has to use special features and some tricks to get precisely the desired molecules. In this exercise you will use the HyperChem modelbuilder, with an assist from the MM+ molecular mechanics, to build some stereoisomers.

Carvone

In this example, the goal will be to produce the two stereoisomers of carvone (2-methyl-5-(1-methyl-ethenyl)-2-cyclohexenone) side-by-side on the screen. The characteristic odor of oil of spearmint is (-)-carvone. Below is (+)-carvone, a flavoring agent of caraway seeds. The ethene group attached at the chiral carbon is out of the page. What we want to do is recreate the same molecule alongside this one with the ethene into the page.

Construct (+)-carvone as shown above by drawing all of the atoms except hydrogen. Add the three double bonds. Use Add H and Model Build command. Rotate the molecule so you can determine the stereochemistry of the chiral carbon. Two techniques can be of assistance here. Sometimes the modelbuilder constructs the molecule with the exo C=C to the left instead of to the right as shown above. You can rotate the whole group by selecting all of the atoms in the side chain including the carbon in the ring. Then use the z-rotate tool and R-drag the group to the orientation above. Remember rotating round a single bond does NOT change the chirality! Secondly, you can display wedges using the drawing tool. Center it over the C-C bond shown and hold the shift key down while you L-click.

On the Display-Labels menu, choose Chirality to show the R, S notation. Is (+)-carvone the R or S enantiomer?

Next you will draw the other enantiomer. Choose Select All to select the entire molecule.

SHORTCUT

If the select cursor is pointing somewhere other than on part of a molecule, clicking the left mouse button will select the entire molecule.

Use the Edit-Copy and Paste functions to create a duplicate of the (+)-carvone. Now you have two identical molecules. If you try to move or rotate them with the appropriate cursors using L-drag, both molecules move. Essentially, with the left mouse button down, you are moving the viewer relative to the entire scene.

To move only one molecule, choose Molecules from the Select menu. Then click on one of the molecules. Now R-Drag using one of the positioning cursors to move only the selected molecule. Use the various cursors to arrange the two molecules side-by-side in some reasonable manner.

Once you have the two identical molecules side-by-side, use the Draw tool. Put the cursor on the chiral carbon atom of one of the molecules. Shift-L-Click to change the chirality of the atom, i.e. click the left mouse button while holding down the shift key.

You may want to convince yourself that these images are enantiomers by trying to superimpose them.

Hexahelicene

Constructing hexahelicene is an interesting challenge. The starting point under normal conditions would be to sketch the molecule, as above, double clicking on each ring to produce a conjugated double bond system in the ring. If HyperChem is then asked to modelbuild the system, it goes a little crazy, folding some rings back upon themselves. The molecule remains planar.

In this case, let a molecular mechanics calculation help you. Remember that if a molecule starts off completely planar, molecular mechanics or quantum mechanics geometry optimizations can't make it non-planar. How do we obtain the spiral effect?

Once you have sketched the molecule, ask HyperChem to Add Hydrogens **without** modelbuilding. Then, take advantage of turning off the "whole molecule translation." On the File-Preferences menu open the Tool box and remove the check from the Whole molecule translation box as shown.

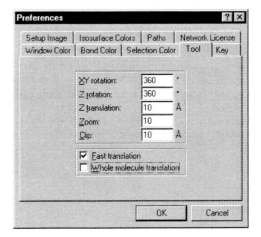

Select three carbon atoms and attached hydrogens at one end of the molecule. Rotate the molecule so it is perpendicular to you; so you see it edge on. Then using the translation tool R-drag the selected group of atoms a short distance out of the plane of the rest of the molecule.

Be sure to recheck the whole molecule translation before you forget!

Choose MM+ molecular mechanics and do a geometry optimization. Set the convergence to 0.01. Within a few minutes, you will have a properly spiraling hexahelicene molecule. As Allinger points out, the success of MM+ in computing the pitch of the spiral is a measure of the balance between the parameters for van der Waals forces and those which are striving to keep the conjugated system planar. Compare your results with the experimental results reported by Linder.

Save this file for later comparison to the mirror image. To produce the mirror image molecule, select three carbon atoms at one end of the molecule. Name the selection using the predefined name PLANE. Deselect the atoms, then on the Edit pull down menu choose "reflect."

This causes all of the atoms in the molecule to be reflected in the defined PLANE. Merge this file with the previously saved version to visualize the mirror images.

References

Vollhardt, K.Peter C.; Schore, Neil E. *Organic Chemistry 2nd ed.* Freeman: New York, 1994, p 1.

Burkert, U.; Allinger, N. L. *Molecular Mechanics*; ACS Monograph 177; American Chemical Society; Washington, DC, 1982, p 152.

Linder, H. J. *Tetrahedron* **1975**, 31, 281.

4. The Steroid Nucleus and Cholesterol

Steroids are an interesting class of molecules where the powerful modelbuilder algorithms of HyperChem don't tend to give the conformation and stereochemistry of the biochemically active forms. It is worthwhile developing a bag of tricks that will allow you to tackle such classes.

The Nucleus

The steroid nucleus consists of three trans-fused cyclohexane rings with cyclopentane also fused into the system to make a tetracyclic molecule. Typically there are two axial methyl groups and two oxygen atoms attached to the rings as shown below. The rings are designated *A, B, C* and *D* left to right.

If one simply starts by sketching the four rings and invoking the modelbuilder (Add H and Model Build), HyperChem cycles through a number of iterations to produce a molecule with the "A" ring in a boat form, not the traditional conformation for a steroid.

A procedure we found to work is to start with a system of four cyclohexane rings. (Yes, all six member rings, read on!) HyperChem will immediately modelbuild this in the proper all-chair conformation. All additional groups are added in steps and the proper geometry obtained by some quick molecular mechanics geometry optimization.

Epiandrosterone

To build epiandrosterone, build four fused six-carbon rings and invoke the modelbuilder. Add H and Model Build. Rotate the structure so you have two rings forward on the left and two rings back on the right. The forward hydrogen on the carbon of the AB rings should point down and the rear one points up.

Using the Draw cursor with carbon the chosen element, click on the appropriate two hydrogens to convert them to the methyl groups sticking up above the molecule. Invoke Add Hydrogen.

In the same way, with oxygen as the chosen element, convert a hydrogen where the OH will be on the A ring to oxygen. On the D ring delete the appropriate hydrogens and add a double bonded oxygen. Finally, in the D ring, remove the CH_2 group adjacent to the –C=O and connect the carbonyl carbon to the next carbon in the ring, closing the five member ring. Invoke Add Hydrogen.

At this point, the molecule has the correct bonds, but the geometry is slightly distorted. Set up an MM+ calculation and optimize the geometry. Verify that the rings are all in the chair form and that the methyl groups are in the correct stereochemistry. Use Display-Labels-Chirality to see how many chiral carbon atoms are present in this structure. Save this structure.

Cholesterol

Next using the previous molecule as a starting point you will build cholesterol. Open the epiandrosterone file if it is not in the workspace. Remove two hydrogen atoms and increase the appropriate C-C to C=C; reduce the C=O to a single bond and convert the O to a carbon. Invoke Add Hydrogen. Do a geometry optimization (MM+) to fine tune the geometry.

Verify that the methyl group on the D ring is in the equatorial position. If it is not, it can be quickly converted using the drawing tool. Place the drawing cursor over the ring carbon holding the methyl group and L-click. This will reorient the axial and equatorial groups. Then on the equatorial methyl group of the D ring, choose one hydrogen to convert to carbon; choose another to build a 2-methylpentyl group. Invoke Add H and Model Build. Optimize the final structure using MM+.

For further exercise, try cortisone, estradiol and testosterone. The structures can be found in any biochemistry book.

Reference

Vollhardt, K. Peter C.; Schore, Neil E. *Organic Chemistry, 2ⁿᵈ ed.;* Freeman: New York, 1994; pp 126-127.

5. Alkaloids: Acetylcholine Impersonators

Acetylcholine is a flexible molecule that must interact with several different active sites. This conclusion is based on the fact that several different types of molecules can compete with acetylcholine in receptor sites.

Nicotine

The pharmacologically active levorotatory form of nicotine is said to impersonate acetylcholine receptors in the brain. You will build and view both forms of nicotine to explore the three dimensional structures of the two optical isomers. Next, you will compare (S)-nicotine with acetylcholine to test the idea that nicotine binds in the same site as acetylcholine.

Nicotine	Acetylcholine

Draw and modelbuild nicotine. Label the chiral centers using Display-Labels-Chirality. Note that HyperChem marks two chiral centers. Nicotine really has only one active chiral center, the one at carbon. The configuration is S (-). The nitrogen does have four different substituents so this arrangement indeed appears to be chiral. However, the lone pair of electrons on nitrogen can rapidly oscillate from one XYZ plane to the other due to a phenomenon called pyramidal inversion and therefore chirality at nitrogen is lost.

If it does not have the correct chirality at carbon, invert the geometry by placing the drawing cursor over the chiral atom and using Shift-L-click. Carry out an MM+ geometry optimization and save the structure.

Experiment with the orientation and display options to enhance the 3-D representation of the isomer. Looking down the bond between the chiral carbon and the pyridine ring, one can see that several different rotational minima are possible. By constraining the torsion angle around this bond, build rotational forms in which the two nitrogen atoms are on the same side of the molecule but in one case the N-CH$_3$ moiety is above the pyridine plane and in the other, below.

For each of these forms, carry out an MM+ geometry optimization and measure the N-N interatomic distance with the select cursor.

Next build acetylcholine. Manipulate the dihedral angles in acetylcholine to see if you can achieve a conformation that resembles nicotine in the distance between the two nitrogen atoms. If you do find a reasonable match, optimize (MM+) the molecular energy using that conformation as a starting point. Measure the distance from the carbonyl oxygen to the nitrogen. How does it compare to the N-N distance in nicotine?

Merge the (S)-nicotine structure file with the acetylcholine structure file. Arrange them so you can see the similarity.

Muscarone

A similar exercise can be performed with muscarone. This molecule has three atoms that seem to play a role in molecular activity.

The distances shown hereare from the Kier book. They are estimated from Extended Hückel calculations. Calculations indicated that the conformation with the $N(CH_3)_3$ over the ring was of much higher energy and could be ignored. You can test this with MM+ calculations.

Using the conformation above as a starting point, minimize the geometry of muscarone. Then, try to adjust torsion angles in acetylcholine to find a conformation with the three active atoms in a similar spatial orientation to muscarone. Optimize the geometry. Compare the O-N distances in both molecules.

References

Kier, Lemont B. *Molecular Orbital Theory in Drug Research*; Academic Press: New York; 1971; pp164-173.

K. Mislow *Pure Appl. Chem.* **1971**, 25, 549-562.

6. Polypeptides and Proteins

HyperChem provides tools for easy construction of polypeptides and proteins. An included database contains a library of amino acid residues that allows you to quickly draw polypeptides in a variety of conformations. The *.HIN files for several larger proteins are included in the HyperChem package. The Protein Database at the National Institutes of Health has many other examples that can be downloaded and worked with in HyperChem.

Several additional visualization tools will also be introduced in these examples. We will start with some small polypeptides.

Nutrasweet™

As a quick example, construct Nutrasweet™ by linking aspartic acid and phenylalanine and converting it to the methyl ester. Whenever you choose a residue to add to a peptide chain, HyperChem adds only the residue, i.e.

$$\begin{array}{ccc} & R & O \\ & | & \nearrow\!\!/ \\ H\!-\!C\!-\!C & \\ & | & \diagdown \\ & NH & \\ & \diagup & \end{array}$$

Before building Nutrasweet, choose Show Hydrogens from the Display menu and choose Symbols from the labels. Try putting glycine on the screen just by itself and carefully look at the atoms. HyperChem adds residues, not amino acids. The next amino acid you choose will be added **at the CO end** of the chain, -NH-CHR-CO-NH-CHR'-CO-, etc.

Now, start a new molecule and choose, from the Amino Acids part of the Database menu, first Asp, then Phe. Once the two linked residues are on the screen, examine the molecule. Note the carboxyl group on the aspartic acid side chain is there as $-CO_2^-$, adding a negative charge to the chain. The HyperChem reference manual describes each residue in detail.

From the Databases menu, choose Make Zwitterion. Look carefully at the chain again, and you'll see that =O has been added to the CO end of the chain, and 2 H have been added to the NH end. This is not quite aspartame - it needs a methyl group at the carboxyl end of the chain to make the methyl ester, so add a C atom to the last O. Then, add H and Model Build.

Bradykinin

Bradykinin is a nine-residue peptide formed by the body in response to wasp stings. It is the source of the pain in a sting! It has the sequence:

arg-pro-pro-gly-phe-ser-pro-phe-arg

To build it, turn off the Show Hydrogens, choose sticks for rendering, and also ribbon from the sticks description menu (sticks tab).

From the Amino Acids display box, under the Databases menu, click on alpha helix. You have the choice of two standard sets of phi, psi angles.

for the alpha helix: phi = -58 and psi = -47 degrees

for the beta sheet: phi and psi both equal 180

If you choose either of these, you still can change the value of omega. If you choose Other, the user can specify all three angles.

From the Amino Acids dialog box, choose Arg, then Pro, etc. If you have sound on your system, you may notice that a bell on the computer chirps each time that you choose proline. This is to let you know that the pyrrolidine ring forces different phi and psi torsion angles and will lead to kinks in the chains you are building.

Once you've constructed the chain, notice that the ribbon gives you the shape of the backbone of the polypeptide. Rebuild the chain with beta sheet, instead of alpha helix and look at the ribbon.

To better observe the kink in the chain you may need to try a longer chain. Try a random15-peptide sequence with no prolines in it, using a beta sheet. No kinks appear. Then try a 15-peptide sequence with a proline in the middle.

Finally, from the Display-Labels dialog box try the additional aids provided for viewing protein structure.

residues - names

residues - sequence

residues - names+sequence

Proteins

Several protein structures are included with HyperChem in the Brookhaven PDB (*.ent) format. Open the file Pdb3cyt.ent in the /Samples/PDB/ subdirectory. This is a Heme-protein with two chains. Buried deep inside the chains is a heme group. See if you can find it. Hint: Turn off the ribbon display if it is still on. Then Select element color from the display menu and set all C, H, O and N atoms to a single color (not red). This should enable you to see where the red iron atoms are located. When finished, be sure to return the element colors to the default settings by clicking Revert on the same menu.

Other large structures can be downloaded from the National Institutes of Health Protein DataBase, Molecules R'Us.

[http://molbio.info.nih.gov/cgi-bin/pdb/]

Type in a key word such as heme or insulin and you will see a list of available structures. You can request them as RawData-Text. Then save the file as a plain text file but with the protein data bank extension .ent (i.e. test.ent). This file can be read directly into HyperChem and manipulated as you would any other file.

7. Nucleotides: DNA and RNA Mutation

Deoxyribonucleotides (DNA) and ribonucleotides (RNA) sequences can be built easily using the HyperChem database Nucleic Acids that contains the necessary residues and terminal or capping groups. In this exercise you will draw a simple four-residue single strand of DNA in the alpha helix conformation. After completing it you will learn how to mutate the structure by replacing one residue with another.

The Database menu for Nucleic Acids is shown below. The bases that are building blocks of DNA are adenine (dA), thymine (dT), guanine (dG) and cytosine (dC). The building blocks of RNA are preceded with a small r.

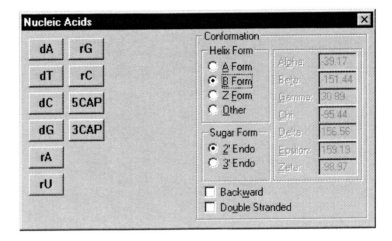

Various conformations can be built by selecting the form of the helix and the sugar. The A form is a right-handed helix with about 11 residues per turn while B has about 10 residues per turn. When Double Strand is checked HyperChem adds the complementary residue, according to Watson-Crick base-pairing rules. When Backward is checked, HyperChem starts polymerization from the 3' end, adding nucleotides to the 5' end.

tRNA

Start with the settings shown above to build up a segment of tRNA. L-click on the RNA bases forming a chain with the following sequence. This was the first nucleotide sequence identified and is part of a 77-

member polynucleotide chain of yeast alanine tRNA.that R. W. Holly and his colleagues reported in 1965. Build it and view the structure.

G-G-G-A-G-A-G-U

Move the Menu dialog box to the side so you can see how the helical structure is built up. When finished, L-click on 3-cap to add the terminating –OH group at the 3' end. (If Backward was checked, use 5' cap to terminate the strand.)

DNA - A Double Helix

When DNA of higher organisms is fragmented for study by density gradient centrifugation, it is usually found that one large main peak is produced along with one or more small satellite peaks of significantly different composition. The satellite peaks of some species exhibit simple repetitive sequences. The satellite DNA of a fruit fly species has the repetitive sequence

A-C-A-A-A-T-T-A-G-C-G

Build up that sequence of DNA residues using the double helix option. What is the sequence order of the complementary residue?

Mutations

Sometimes when studying proteins, it is of interest to "mutate" a DNA strand. This means that one residue is replaced by another. A common kind of mutation is the transversional mutation in which a pyrimidine-purine pair replaces a purine-pyrimidine pair, e.g. A...T to T...A

To do this, check Residues on the Select menu. Select one of the A residues by L-clicking on one of its atoms. Notice that the entire residue is selected. The status line will indicate which residue has been selected. Then go to the Databases menu and choose Mutate. Change the Adenine residue to thymine by selecting dT. Change its complement to dA using the same method.

Additional Visualization Tools

Hydrogen bonds can be displayed by checking Recompute Hydrogen Bonds on the Display menu.

Add Counter Ions on the Databases menu will add a sodium ions to the phosphate oxygen atoms.

The atoms of the backbone can be displayed in a different color using Select-Backbone followed by Display-Color and your choice of color.

References

Holly, R. W.; et al. *Science* **1965,** 147, 1462-1465.

Lehninger, Albert L. *Biochemistry, 2nd ed.;* Worth: New York, 1975.

8. Building Coordination Complexes

Coordination compounds can present a particular challenge for the HyperChem modelbuilder because there are so many geometries possible. For example, consider a metal ion with five ligands attached. The limiting structures possible are the trigonal bipyramid and the square-based pyramid. In this exercise you will build complexes of each type learning how to constrain geometry to produce a good starting structure for later calculations.

Problems can also arise when chelating ligands such as ethylenediamine are introduced. Getting the correct geometry at the metal center can sometimes be facilitated using a modeling technique called docking.

Five-coordinate Geometry

Five coordinate complexes can exhibit geometry ranging from "perfect" trigonal bypyramids to "perfect" square-based pyramids. Intermediate distorted structures also are known. Pentachlorocuprate(II) and pentacyanonickelate(II) will serve as example of the limiting structures possible for complexes that contain five ligands. $[CuCl_5]^{3-}$ is bypyramidal while $[Ni(CN)_5]^{3-}$ exhibits a square-based pyramid geometry.

Check the Allow Ions box on the periodic table. Construct the five coordinate copper complex. Use the modelbuilder to see that the geometry produced is indeed the correct one. Save the file for later use.

Build the nickel complex in the same manner. Note that modelbuilder again produces a bipyramid, the incorrect geometry in this case. Set the selection tool to atoms rather than molecules. To get the correct geometry select the nickel atom. Use the build menu to constrain the geometry to octahedral.

Deselect nickel by clicking anywhere in the workspace. Invoke the modelbuilder again. You should now see the correct structure. Save this file as well.

Next we will optimize the geometry using a semi-empirical method that was parameterized for transition metals. Select PM3 from the set up menu and specify the following options. Note: PM3 was not parameterized for the transition metals in earlier versions of HyperChem. You could then try ZINDO/1 although it takes longer!

Complex	Total Charge	Spin Multiplicity
Copper	-3	2
Nickel	-3	1

You will see a warning message for the copper complex. It is a reminder that there is an odd number of electrons in this case. For the copper complex that is correct so press continue.

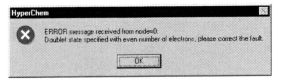

Set the SCF Convergence limit to 1e-5 or 1000 iterations. Do the optimization to at least 0.1 rms convergence limit and record the geometric information specific in the table below. How close are these two complexes to the limiting cases?

	Metal to axial ligand distance (Å)	Metal to equatorial ligand distance (Å)	Angles (°)
Copper Complex			eq-M-eq
			ax-M-eq
Nickel Complex			eq-M-eq
			ax-M-eq

Square Planar Geometry

Problems arise when trying to constrain geometry when a cyclic system is present. Complexes with chelating ligands like ethylenediamine (en) need more than the modelbuilder to produce the correct geometry. In the next section we will see how docking molecules can be used overcome the problems.

Dichloro(ethylenediamine)platinum(II) will be used as an example. Platinum is square planar in this complex. Draw the structure and use modelbuilder to obtain a starting geometry. You will note that the geometry around platinum is tetrahedral! Try to constrain the platinum to square planar. What happens? Probably nothing! Once the ring is closed you cannot constrain the geometry.

Now try it a different way. Draw platinum with two chlorine atoms and two NH_2 groups. Select the platinum and constrain the geometry to square planar. De-select platinum and modelbuild. You should now have a planar platinum. Save this structure.

Next, build the platinum ethylenediamine fragment shown on the right and optimize the geometry using MM+. Save this molecule.

Merge the two files so both pieces are in the workspace. We will use the docking process to get the two fragments positioned. With the select tool set to Atoms and Multiple Selections, select (in exactly this order) Pt-N1-N2 of the first structure and then Pt-N1-N2 of the second structure. Next, go to the Display menu and choose Overlay. This will superimpose the two planes defined as you selected the atoms. L-click in the workspace to remove the selections. The only thing that remains is to carefully delete the duplicate atoms: two nitrogens and one platinum. When you delete nitrogen, its hydrogens will automatically be removed. Sometimes it is necessary to reconnect bonds. Do **not** model build or you will be back to a tetrahedral geometry! Save this structure for later use.

Optimizing this structure with MM+ requires constraints to keep the square planar geometry. To do this select one Cl-Pt-N angle and Use the Select-Name selection option to name it Angle1. Then select the other Cl-Pt-N angle and name it Angle2.

On the Setup menu choose Restraints. Move Angle1 and Angle2 to the Restraints box with the Add button. Set the restrained value to 180 and the Force Constant to a large value such as 1000. L-click OK.

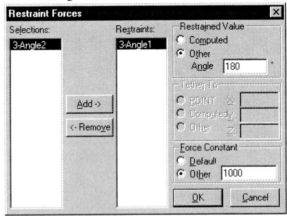

Now you can do an MM+ optimization without losing the square planar structure. When it is completed, once again select Setup-Restraints and remove the two restraints. Following this, do a single point calculation to get the energy.

If you have semi-empirical parameters for platinum, the same technique can be used to optimize the geometry and compute spectra. See the HyperChem manuals for instructions on how to modify the parameter set. Many parameters are available on the World Wide Web. The Molecular Modeling Research server at the University of Sassari-Italy

has pointers to many of these.
[http://antas.agraria.uniss.it/molec_db.html]

Reference

Huheey, J. E.; Keiter, E. A.; Keiter, R. L. *Inorganic Chemistry, 4th ed.* HarperCollins: New York; 1993, p 480

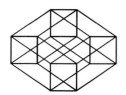

Chapter 2
Molecular Geometry and Properties

"We are perhaps not far removed from the time when we shall be able to submit the bulk of chemical phenomena to calculation." - J. L. Gay-Lussac, 1808.

"All of chemistry, and with it crystallography, would become a branch of mathematical analysis which, like astronomy, would enable us to predict the character of any new compound and possibly the source from which it might be anticipated." - Charles Babbage, 1838.

The dream of early 19th century scientists is becoming reality in the late 20th century. The "success" of computer-assisted chemistry in predicting properties has led to many advancements toward computer-aided molecular design.

Once the basic methods of modeling the three-dimensional structure of molecules are in hand, we can proceed to measure geometric properties such as bond lengths and bond angles. In the next few lessons we will again begin with some simple molecules to explore periodic trends in size and the influence of this on molecular geometry. We will also be comparing various computational methods to see which ones give the most reasonable results when compared to experiment.

Measuring properties related to the structures will also be explored as you learn to display charges and to extract information from a HyperChem log file and to use simple scripts to obtain specific calculated values. In this chapter you will see how proton and electron affinities, ionization potentials and bond enthalpies can be calculated using information generated by quantum calculations. Later chapters will introduce other properties that can be successfully computed.

9. Periodicity: Bond Lengths and Bond Angles

Periodicity has long been recognized as the tool that chemists can use to bring some order to investigating the chemistry of more than one-hundred elements comprising the realm of "inorganic chemistry." Such studies provide useful tools for understanding a wide array of chemical principles. In this exercise you will explore some simple trends in bond lengths and bond angles.

Computational models gain validity by being tried against large volumes of experimental data. Semi-empirical methods are faster than *ab initio* "from the beginning" calculations because they rely on some experimental parameters as a starting point. As such, they are necessarily developed with particular kinds of molecules in mind. In this exercise we are going to compare how several of the semi-empirical methods compare with known values of bond lengths and bond angles.

Bond Lengths

Construct and use the modelbuilder to get a beginning structure for each of the molecules in the table below. Measure the modelbuilder bond length indicated using the Select tool. L-click near the center of the bond. The bond will be highlighted in green (unless the default color scheme was changed). The length will show on the status line below the workspace.

Optimize each molecule using the semi-empirical method indicated. Record the values in the appropriate column. Experimental values are given in Ångstsrom units.

Bond Angles

Bond angles can be measured with the select tool by L-clicking on the three atoms or by L-dragging from the first to the third atom in the angle. The angle will be highlighted and the bond angle will be shown on the status line.

Measure the angles indicated in the optimized structures. Compare angles with the same central atom for periodic trends.

Overall, which method seems to give the most reliable results for this small set of compounds?

Bond Lengths

Molecule	Bond Length	Model builder	MM+	AM1	PM3	Exp. (Å)
$CH_3-CH_2-CH_3$	C-C					1.53
CH_3-O-CH_3	C-O					1.42
CH_3-S-CH_3	C-S					1.81
$CH_3-Se-CH_3$	C-Se					1.94
SCl_2	S-Cl					2.01
$SeCl_2$	Se-Cl					2.16
OCl_2	O-Cl					1.70
OF2	O-F					1.42
H_2O	O-H					0.96
H_2S	S-H					1.35
H_2Se	Se-H					1.46
PF_3	P-F					1.56
PCl_3	P-Cl					2.04
PBr_3	P-Br					2.22
PI_3	P-I					2.46

Bond Angles

Molecule	Bond Angle	Model builder	MM+	AM1	PM3	Exp. (°)
$CH_3-CH_2-CH_3$	C-C-C					109.5
CH_3-O-CH_3	C-O-C					112
CH_3-S-CH_3	C-S-C					99.1
$CH_3-Se-CH_3$	C-Se-C					96.2
SCl_2	Cl-S-Cl					102.8
$SeCl_2$	Cl-Se-Cl					99.6
OCl_2	Cl-O-Cl					110.8
OF_2	F-O-F					103.2
H_2O	H-O-H					104.5
H_2S	H-S-H					92.3
H_2Se	H-Se-H					91.0
PF_3	F-P-F					97.8
PCl_3	Cl-P-Cl					100.3
PBr_3	Br-P-Br					101.5
PI_3	I-P-I					102.0

Testing Other Trends

Partial multiple bonding with phosphorus d orbitals is used to explain the 94° and 98° bond angles of PH_3 and PF_3 compared to the 107° and 102° angles of NH_3 and NF_3 respectively. Carry out AM1, STO-3G and 6-31G** geometry optimizations to see how well *ab initio* calculations can reproduce the angle orders. For the latter calculation, be certain to use accelerated convergence and plan on a few hours' run with a 486 processor!

Molecule	AM1	STO-3G	6-31G**	Exp. (°)
PH_3				93.3
PF_3				97.8
NH_3				106.7
NF_3				102.2

Partial double bonding involving d orbitals is used to explain the fact that one might expect on an electronegativity basis to have the order

$$OF_2 \quad < \quad OCl_2 \quad < \quad OH_2$$

but finds

$$OF_2 \quad < \quad OH_2 \quad < \quad OCl_2$$

Again, carry out AM1, STO-3G and 6-31G** geometry optimizations to see how well *ab initio* calculations can reproduce the angle orders.

Molecule	AM1	STO-3G	6-31G**	Exp. (°)
OCl_2				110.9
OH_2				104.5
OF_2				103.1

References

Purcell, K. F.; Kotz, J.C. *Inorganic Chemistry;* Saunders: Philadelphia, 1977.

Lange's Handbook of Chemistry 13th ed.; McGraw-Hill: New York, 1985.

Dictionary of Inorganic Compounds; Macintyre, J. E., Exec. Ed.; Chapman & Hall: London, 1992.

10. Valence Shell Electron Repulsion Theory

Although the fine details of molecular structure such as precise bond angles and bond lengths are important, our first mental impression of a molecule has to do with its general shape. Predicting the shape of a molecule, or of the bonds around a particular atom in a particular setting, is the second skill a chemist acquires, after learning to wash glassware. In this exercise, you'll look at a collection of molecules containing single bonds to see how well you and the HyperChem modelbuilder program can predict shapes.

Valence shell electron pair repulsion theory (VSEPR) can be used to predict the shapes of molecules. The theory states that the most stable covalent molecule is one in which the electron pairs about the central atom arrange themselves so as to minimize electrostatic repulsion. There are two things we must distinguish here: the geometry of the orbitals about the central atom and the shape of the molecule. The former depends on the total number of electron pairs in the valence shell of the central atom. The latter refers to the arrangement of the bonded atoms. When these are the same, the geometry of the orbitals is the same as the shape of the molecule. However, many compounds are known in which some of the valence electrons are not shared with other atoms. Then, the shape of the molecule can differ depending on where these non-bonding pairs or "lone pairs" are found. In such cases, the minimum energy arrangement is one in which the lone pairs can occupy the greatest angular volume.

Table 1 below contains examples of some of the possible combinations of bond pairs and lone pairs commonly occurring in singly bonded molecules. For each, predict the shape of the orbitals. Then draw the best possible geometry of the molecules using VSEPR. Show other possible positions the lone pairs could occupy in cases where there is one than one is indicated in parentheses after the formula. For example, the three ClF_3 structures are shown below. **This should be completed before coming to the computer lab.**

$$
\begin{array}{ccc}
\underset{\underset{\text{Lp}}{\overset{\text{Lp}}{\underset{F}{\overset{F//}{\text{Cl}}}}}{\text{F}} - F
&
\underset{\underset{F}{\overset{\text{Lp}}{\underset{F}{\overset{F//}{\text{Cl}}}}}{\text{F}} - Lp
&
\underset{\underset{\text{Lp}}{\overset{F}{\underset{F}{\overset{F//}{\text{Cl}}}}}{\text{F}} - Lp
\end{array}
$$

Using Modelbuilder Models

From the Setup menu, select AM1. For neutral molecules, under options set the charge to zero and the multiplicity to 1. For the anions, set the charge to the value indicated. The multiplicity remains 1 since there are no unpaired electrons in these species.

Use modelbuilder to construct each molecule including the lone pairs. Determine its AM1 single point energy. Record the energy below the structure. Determine if your prediction of the "best geometry" is the lowest energy form.

Optimizing Geometry

Starting with the **best (i.e. lowest energy)** modelbuilder shape for each molecule in the table, carry out a geometry optimization to see what a semi-empirical molecular orbital method such as AM1 can do to give more realistic result. To avoid confusion, it is best to remove the lone pairs prior to doing this calculation. While these electrons are accounted for in the calculation, their position is not shown correctly in the resulting geometry. Record the energy in the table. In your notes, record the shape of the optimized molecular structure. Use it to answer the questions below.

Dipole Moments

Use a simple script file below determine the dipole moment of each optimized structure. Open Notepad or some other text editor. Enter the following line and save the file in the Scripts subdirectory of HyperChem calling it dipole.scr.

query-value dipole-moment

With the optimized structure in the workspace, select Script from the top menu and then open dipole.scr. Record the dipole moments in the Table 2 below.

Alternatively, the dipole moment can be obtained from a log file.

Questions

Were your pre-lab predictions of the best structure correct? If not, can you identify where you went wrong?

For each of the molecules, describe how the geometry changes on optimization. Did optimization give a shape more closely resembling the expected VSEPR results? Are bond lengths the same for axial and equatorial positions? Did the angles change? Account for variations in terms of VSEPR. Are there any cases where AM1 gives totally incorrect results?

Compare your dipole moment results with the literature values. Look for trends rather than exact values.

Further Investigations

Investigate some "mixed" compounds such as $TeCl_2(CH_3)_2$ or $IBrCl_3^-$ to see how the size of the peripheral atoms or groups influences geometry.

Investigate the steric effects of π clouds by comparing $CH_2=SF_4$, $O=SF_4$ and $:SF_4$

References

Lange's Handbook of Chemistry, 13th ed. McGraw-Hill: New York, 1985.

Dictionary of Inorganic Compounds; MacIntyre, J.E., Exec. Ed.; Chapman & Hall: London, 1992.

Wells, A. F. *Structural Inorganic Chemistry, 3rd Ed.;* Oxford University Press: London, 1962

Table 1. Representative Compounds for VSEPR Study

Molecule	#Valence Electron Pairs	#Lone Pairs	Geometry of Orbitals	Predicted Best Structure (kcal/mol)	AM1 Single Point Energy (kcal/mol)	AM1 Optimized Energy (kcal/mol)
BeF_2						
BF_3						
NH_3						
PH_3						
CH_4						
H_2O						
H_2S						
SF_4 (2) LP – eq						
SF_4 LP - ax						
ClF_5						
SF_6						

ClF_3 (3) LP eq-eq					
ClF_3 LP eq-ax					
ClF_3 LP ax-ax					
I_3^- (3) LP eq-eq-eq					
I_3^- LP eq-eq-ax					
I_3^- LP ax-eq-ax					
BrF_4^- (2) LP ax-ax					
LP ax-eq					

Table 2. Dipole Moments

Compound	Experimental Dipole Moment, μ in Debyes	AM1 Dipole Moment, μ in Debyes
BeF_2	Not stable in gas phase	
BF_3	0	
NH_3	1.007	
PH_3	2.292	
CH_4	0	
H_2O	1.85	
H_2S		
ClF_3	0.6	
SF_4	0.632	
SeF_4	1.78	No AM1 parameters
PCl_5	0.9	
PF_5	0	
ClF_5	0.55	
PCl_3	0.78	
PBr_3	0.5	
SF_6	0	

11. Ionization Energy

The energy required to remove an electron from an atom or ion is called the ionization energy or ionization potential. There are several approaches to the calculation of the ionization energies of molecules. Koopmans' theorem relates the ionization energy directly to the energy of the highest occupied molecular orbital:

$$I = -\varepsilon_{HOMO}$$

Estimates of ionization potential from orbital energies work well for compounds if adding or removing one electron does not alter the molecular orbitals. It cannot be applied to ionization from MO's which mainly consist of d orbitals of transition metal elements. In these cases, the ΔSCF method is used. A separate calculation is carried out on the neutral and on the ionized state. The ionization potential is estimated as the difference in total energy between the two calculations.

We will try calculating the ionization potential of some organic and main group inorganic compounds using Koopmans' theorem. Typical errors in ionization potentials for many organic compounds are ±0.5 eV using MNDO, AM1 or PM3. The ionization potentials of the compounds in the table below are from the NIST WebBook at [http://webbook.nist.gov/chemistry].

Draw and model build each compound. Do a geometry optimization using AM1 or PM3. After the optimization select Compute-Orbitals and record the energy of the highest occupied molecular orbital.

Graph the data. Is there a linear correlation between the ionization potential and the negative of the HOMO energy? Do the values you obtained fall within the "typical" range of values reported for organic compounds, i.e. IP ± 0.5 eV?

References

NIST Chemistry WebBook, NIST Standard Reference Database Number 69, March 1998, Eds. W.G. Mallard and P.J. Linstrom.

Yoshida, S.; Sakai, S.; Kobayashi, H. *Electronic Processes in Catalysis*; VCH: Weinheim, 1994; Chapter 2.

Compound	IP (eV)	−ε HOMO (eV)	Δ E
1,2,3,4-tetramethylbenzene	8.16		
Methoxybenzene	8.20		
1,4-diethylbenzene	8.40		
1,3 diethylbenzene	8.49		
Ethylbenzene	8.77		
Phenylacetylide	8.82		
Toluene	8.83		
Bromobenzene	9.00		
1,4 difluorobenzene	9.16		
Benzene	9.24		
1,2,3,5-tetrafluorobenzene	9.55		
2-fluorobenzonitrile	9.78		
4-cyanobenzoic acid	10.00		

Try the following compounds of the main group elements.

	IP (eV)	−ε HOMO (eV)	Δ E
Ozone, O_3	12.53		
Oxygen, O_2	12.07		
Carbon monoxide, CO	14.01		
Carbon dioxid, CO_2	13.78		
Carbon disulfide, CS_2	10.07		
Boron trichloride, BCl_3	11.60		
Phosphorus trichloride, PCl_3	9.90		
Ammonia, NH_3	10.07		
Hydrogen iodide, HI	10.39		
Hydrogen chloride, HCl	12.74		
Hydrogen fluoride, HF	16.03		
Water, H_2O	12.62		
Hydrogen sulfide, H_2S	10.46		

Does the method you used seem to work equally well for organic and inorganic compounds?

12. Proton Affinity

Gas phase proton affinity studies may seem far removed from studying acid-base chemistry in solutions but they can provide a valuable tool to understanding the inherent property without the complication of solvent effects.

Formally, the proton affinity (PA) is defined by the relationship between the enthalpy of formation of BH^+ and its neutral counterpart, B. This is the negative of the enthalpy change of the hypothetical protonation reaction:

$$B + H^+ = BH^+ \qquad\qquad \Delta_{rxn}H = -PA$$

$$PA = \Delta_f H^\circ(B) + \Delta_f H^\circ(H^+) - \Delta_f H^\circ(BH^+)$$

Dewar and Dieter have carried out an extensive study of proton affinities using the AM1 semi-empirical molecular orbital method. More recently, Szafran and Koput looked at the proton affinities of mono-substituted pyridines using both PM3 and AM1, concluding that AM1 was the superior method. In both papers, the experimental heat of formation for H^+ is used since the semi-empirical methods do a poor job of estimating that value. $\Delta H_f(H^+)$ is given as 367.2 kcal/mol. In this exercise you will look at part of Dewar and Dieter's work and compare further the relative effectiveness of the AM1 to determine gas phase proton affinities.

First you will obtain data for some monosubstituted pyridines and compare your results to those obtained by Szafran and Koput. Then you will use a set of hydrocarbons reported by Dewar and Dieter to determine if AM1 is also a good tool for that type of compounds. If time permits, the latter set should be studied using another method such as PM3 to see which gives the better results.

For the pyridines we will also invoke the HyperChem module to plot the 3-D isosurface of the electrostatic potential for the neutral species to demonstrate how this property can be used to visualize the site of a reaction. The electrostatic potential indicates what a reactant "sees" as it approaches the molecule.

Monosubstituted Pyridines

Draw each structure and use the modelbuilder in HyperChem to obtain a starting geometry. Optimize the structure using AM1 and determine its heat of formation.

Under the Compute menu select Plot Molecular Properties. On the
Molecular Properties menu select Electrostatic Potential and then 3-D
Isosurface. Under Mapped Functions Options, check the box Display
Range Legend. Then L-click OK. If you have not changed any of the
color options, the pink color shows the region that has a negative
electrostatic potential. The status line will indicate the range of values
of the mapped function. Record the minimum (most negative) value.

Protonate each structure at the pyridine nitrogen. Change the charge to
+1 and the multiplicity to 1 using the options box of Setup. Optimize
the protonated species and record the heats of formation.

Compound	Electrostatic Potential at Nitrogen	$\Delta_f H$ B (kcal/mol) experimental	$\Delta_f H$ BH^+ (kcal/mol) experimental	$\Delta_f H$ B (kcal/mol) AM1	$\Delta_f H$ BH^+ (kcal/mol) AM1
Pyridine		33	178		
2-CH$_3$		23.7	164		
2-CN		67	225		
2-Cl		25	176		
2-NO$_2$		na	na		
2-OCH$_3$		26.7	170		

Calculate the proton affinities from your data using $\Delta_f H$ (H^+) = 367.2
kcal/mol. Compare your results with the work of Szafran and Koput as
well as the experimental values. Do the results fall within the
experimental range in all cases? How does electrostatic potential
correlate with the proton affinity?

Compound	Electrostatic Potential	Proton Affinity (kcal/mol) AM1	Proton Affinity (kcal/mol) Szafran and Koput	Proton Affinity (kcal/mol) Experimental
2-NO$_2$			200.9	
2-CN			206.8	207.1 ± 1.6
2-Cl			211.8	213.7 ± 1.6
Pyridine			215.1	219.2 ± 1.7
2-OCH$_3$			216.2	220.7 ± 1.7
2-CH$_3$			219	222.7 ± 2.0

The Alkane Series

After reproducing some of the results of Szafran and Koput, carry out a comparison of proton affinity results with AM1 and PM3 on the set of hydrocarbons presented in the Dewar and Dieter paper. The experimental values were reported in that paper.

You can take advantage of Dynamic Data Exchange (DDE) in HyperChem to collect this information in an Excel spreadsheet and compute the desired proton affinities. The procedure is to collect the molecules and the conjugates in individual .HIN files. Put the names of the files into a spreadsheet and launch an Excel macro to systematically carry out the calculations. Remember that the charge must be changed for the protonated species.

Reference

Dewar, M.J.S.; Dieter, K.M. *J. Am. Chem. Soc.* **1986**, 108, 8075-8086.

Molecule/ Protonated Structure	AM1 PA (kcal/mol)	PM3 PA (kcal/mol)	Expt. PA (kcal/mol)	AM1 Error	PM3 Error
Methane/ CH_5^+			132.0		
Ethane / $CH_3CH_4^+$			143.6		
Ethene / $CH_3CH_2^+$			162.6		
Ethyne / $CH_2=CH^+$			153.3		
Propene / $CH_3^+CHCH_3$			179.5		
Propyne / $CH_2CH^+=CH_2$			182.0		
Benzene / $C_6H_7^+$			181.3		
Toluene / Para – H See below			189.8		
Naphthalene / 1-H See below			194.7		

13. Electron Affinity

The electron affinity, EA, of a molecule is a quantity that is analogous to the ionization energy for positive ions. That is, the electron affinity is equal to the energy difference between the enthalpy of formation of a neutral species and the enthalpy of formation of the negative ion of the same structure. The electron affinity is defined as the negative of the zero Kelvin (0 K) enthalpy change for the electron attachment reaction:

$$M + e^- \rightarrow M^- \qquad\qquad \Delta_{rxn}H = -EA$$

$$-EA = \Delta_f H°(M^-) - \Delta_f H°(M) - \Delta_f H°(e^-)$$

The value for $\Delta_f H°(e^-)$ defined is zero at 0 K but since most heats of formation are reported at 298K, the integrated heat capacity of an electron gas is required to compare values we will be obtaining from the molecular modeling in this exercise.

The National Institute of Standards and Technology (NIST) Web page has an extensive discussion of conventions used for relating gas phase ion data. [http://webbook.nist.gov/chemistry/ion/] They use the "ion convention" commonly used by scientists studying physics and chemistry in reporting the electron affinity data in the table. Using that convention, a value of 3.145 kJ/mol (= 0.752 kcal/mol = 0.033 eV) should be used here for the integrated heat capacity (e.g. heat of formation) of an electron gas at 298 K.

Computation

Draw and modelbuild the molecules listed in the table. Optimize the geometry using AM1 or PM3. Use a SCF convergence limit of 1e-5 and iteration limit of 100. Use a script file to extract the gas phase heat of formation. All of the neutral species except NO have a spin multiplicity of 1; the multiplicity of NO is 2.

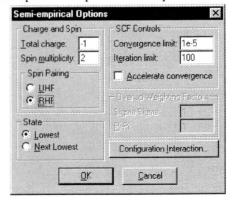

Then, use Setup-Semi-Empirical-Method-Options to change the charge on the species to –1 and the multiplicity to 2 or 1 in the case of NO⁻. Optimize the negative ion and extract its heat of formation.

Calculate the electron

affinity in kcal/mol. Use an appropriate conversion factor to change it to eV/molecule for comparison to table values.

Molecule	$\Delta_f H$ neutral molecule (kcal/mol)	$\Delta_f H$ anion (kcal/mol)	Electron Affinity (eV)	$\Delta_f H$ neutral molecule. Experiment (kcal/mol)	Electron Affinity, Experiment (eV)
CO				-26.42	1.37
CS				+67.00	1.6, 0.2
CO_2				-94.05	-1.6, -0.6
CS_2				+27.95	0.512
COS				-33.08	0.461
SO_2				-70.94	1.1
NO				+21.58	0.026
BCl_3				-96.31	0.33±0.20
PF_3				-229.07	-1.0
PCl_3				-69.00	0.82±0.10
PBr_3				-34.90	1.59±0.15

Do the modeled values for the heat of formation parallel the experimental values?

How do the calculated values for electron affinity compare with the values in the table?

References

NIST Chemistry WebBook, NIST Standard Reference Database Number 69, March 1998, Eds. W.G. Mallard and P.J. Linstrom.

Pearson. R. G., *Chemical Hardness*; Wiley-VCH: New York, 1997.

14. Periodicity of Bond Enthalpy

The bond energy of hydrogen to the main group elements varies as a function for both period and family. In this exercise you will compute the average E-H bond energy for the main group elements for which parameters are available in HyperChem. To do so you will need the binding energy for each molecule. This is the energy reported on the status line after a geometry optimization is completed. It is computed as the difference between the total energy of the system after optimization minus the energy of the isolated atoms. For example, in the case of methane.

Binding energy	=	Total Energy	-	Isolated Atom Energy
-392.37 kcal	=	-4163.35 kcal	-	-3770.98 kcal

This represents the energy released in the bond formation process:

$$C \; + \; 4\,H \quad \rightarrow \quad CH_4$$

Although the step-wise dissociation process would lead to different energies for each step, we will compute the average bond enthalpy as the negative of the binding energy divided by the number of bonds to hydrogen. This would represent the average energy needed to break a bond.

$$392.37/4 \; = \; 98.09 \text{ kcal/mol}$$

Computation

Draw and modelbuild each of the hydrides in the table. It is not necessary to include lone pairs on the models. They will be included in the computation. Use PM3 for this exercise since it has the most complete set of parameters for the main group elements.

Optimize each structure and record the binding energy from the status line in the table below. Also observe the geometry of each molecule. Calculate the average E-H bond energy from the above data. The experimental values for these compounds should be readily available in any chemistry handbook or inorganic chemistry text book.

Present your results using an appropriate two- or three-dimensional graph. Discuss trends you observe and comment on any anomalies.

Group IIIA	Group IVA	Group V A	Group VI A	Group VII A
	CH_4	NH_3	H_2O	HF
AlH_3	SiH_4	PH_3	H_2S	HCl
GaH_3	GeH_4	AsH_3	H_2Se	HBr
InH_3	SnH_4	SbH_3	H_2Te	HI

15. Structure-Stability Relationships

An active and growing field of interest in chemistry is the search for ligands that exhibit selective preference for certain metal ions. Much effort has been focused on the design of macrocyclic ethers because of their high selectivity for alkali and alkaline earth metal ions. Some of these cyclic ethers adopt a crown-like configuration - hence the name "crown ethers." An example, 18-crown-6, is shown below. The "18" refers to the total number of atoms in the macrocycle and "crown-6" indicates 6 oxygen coordination sites. The size of the hole in this crown is about 310 pm so the potassium ion with a diameter of about 305 pm just fits in the hole.

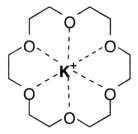

Potassium 18-crown-6

The purpose of this exercise is to investigate the relationship between the ionic radius and the computed energies for a series of compounds. For this study, you will use molecular mechanics. The structure files (*.hin) for each complex will be provided by the Instructor and are the "global minimum" conformations. Parameter files will be modified to include some of the reported literature values.

You will use an Excel macro to obtain data from HyperChem. The macro will issue commands to HyperChem to compute energies for the series of compounds of interest. The information generated by HyperChem will be sent back to the Excel spreadsheet for analysis. The equilibrium constants for some of the compounds are available in the review by Poonia and Bajaj and will be considered in the data analysis.

Modifying Parameter Files

Refer to the HyperChem reference manuals for specific directions about modifying and compiling the parameter files. The added parameters that need to be added are shown in Table 1 at the end of this exercise.

Setting Up HyperChem

Set up HyperChem to do molecular mechanics MM+ calculations. Use a convergence limit of 0.01. On the file menu, open the directory containing the crown.hin files on your system. Alternatively, the macro shown below can be modified to show the full path.

Open each file including the free ligand and look at each of the models using the spheres rendering option. Use the rotate tools to move it around. Describe the geometry about the central ion for each of the complexes and the general conformation of the ring. For example, is it planar, puckered or some other conformation?

Using the Macro

Make the HyperChem screen smaller by L-dragging the cursor from the lower right hand corner until the HyperChem screen fits in the top half of the screen. Open Excel in the lower half and the spreadsheet Crown.xls. The spreadsheet already contains some of the data you will use in the analysis.

	A	B	C	D	E	F	G	H	I
1	Molecule	Total Energy	Stretch	Bend	Torsion	vdW	Radius	log K (water)	log K(MeOH/water)
2	crown								
3	Li-18c6						0.76		
4	Na-18c6						1.02	0.80	2.76
5	K-18c6						1.38	2.03	4.33
6	Rb-18c6						1.52	1.56	3.46
7	Cs-18c6						1.67	0.99	2.84
8	Mg-18c6						0.72		
9	Ca-18c6						1.00	0.50	2.51
10	Sr-18c6						1.18	2.72	5.00
11	Ba-18c6						1.36	3.87	6.00

In the Excel Crown.xls worksheet L-click on cell A2 that contains the first file name, containing the free ligand. The cell should be "boxed" once selected. Then select Tools - Macro and start the macro.

The macro instructs HyperChem to open each file, do a single point energy calculation and return the results to the spreadsheet. When the macro finishes, save the spreadsheet to **your disk** giving it a new name. Please do not overwrite the original spreadsheet.

Data Analysis

Prepare appropriate graphs of energy or equilibrium constant versus the ionic radii to answer the questions below.

From the spreadsheet data, describe the relationship between the total energy and the ionic radii? At what radius does the most stable complex seem to form? Is this consistent with the equilibrium constant values? i.e. Is the minimum energy system favored in the actual chemical equilibrium?

Describe the relationship between the radii and each of the component energies calculated? Which one (if any) seems to be most important in accounting for the general shape of the total energy vs. radii curve? How does the crown molecule adjust to the presence of the ion? Do the bonds stretch making the molecule larger or does some other change account for the pattern observed?

Further Study

Build and minimize a model of the crown ether designated as 14-crown-4. Obtain a minimum energy structure for the crown ether and then build models for the alkali metal salts. Predict which alkali metal might be expected to form the most stable complex.

References

Hay, B P.; Rustad, J. R.; Hostetler, Charles, J., *J. Am. Chem. Soc.* **1993**, 115, 11158-11164.

Huheey, J. E.; Keiter, E. A.; Keiter, R. L. *Inorganic Chemistry, 4th ed.* HarperCollins: New York, 1993.

Poonia, N. S.; Bajaj, A. B. *Chem. Reviews*, 1979, 79(5), 389-430.

Control-R	Compute.Results
Channel	=OpenFile()
	=IF(ISERROR(Channel))
	=RETURN()
	=END.IF()
	=EXECUTE(Channel,"[query-response-has-tag(no)]")
	=WHILE(NOT(ISBLANK(SELECTION())))
Command	=EXECUTE(Channel,"[file-format(hin)][open-file("&SELECTION()&".hin)][do-single-point]")
	=FORMULA.ARRAY(REQUEST(Channel,"total-energy"),"rc[1]")
	=FORMULA.ARRAY(REQUEST(Channel,"stretch-energy"),"rc[2]")
	=FORMULA.ARRAY(REQUEST(Channel,"bend-energy"),"rc[3]")
	=FORMULA.ARRAY(REQUEST(Channel,"torsion-energy"),"rc[4]")
	=FORMULA.ARRAY(REQUEST(Channel,"nonbond-energy"),"rc[5]")
	=SELECT("r[1]c")
	=NEXT()
	=TERMINATE(Channel)
	=RETURN()
	OpenFIle
NewChan	=INITIATE("HyperChem","System")
	=IF(ISERROR(NewChan))
	=IF(ISERROR(EXEC("c:\chem\ship\chem",1)))
	=RETURN(NewChan)
	=END.IF()
	=RETURN(INITIATE("HyperChem","System"))
	=END.IF()
	=RETURN(NewChan)

Table 1. Modifications made to MM+ Parameter file

Mmptyp.txt

The type file was modified to include the missing ions. In some cases, the element symbol was already in use for a different element (e.g. na is defined as azo nitrogen) so numbers were used to distinguish the ions (e.g. na1 for sodium).

```
li     6.941        76. lithium ion
na1    23.990       77. sodium ion
k      39.098       78. potassium ion
rb     85.468       79. rubidium ion
cs     132.905      80. cesium ion
ca2    40.078       81. calcium ion
sr     87.620       82. strontium ion
ba     137.330      83. barium ion
mg2    24.301       84. magnesium ion
```

Mmpben.txt

```
li    o2   c4   0.400    112.000   0.000    0.000
na1   o2   c4   0.400    112.000   0.000    0.000
k     o2   c4   0.400    112.000   0.000    0.000
rb    o2   c4   0.400    112.000   0.000    0.000
cs    o2   c4   0.400    112.000   0.000    0.000
mg2   o2   c4   0.400    112.000   0.000    0.000
ca2   o2   c4   0.400    112.000   0.000    0.000
sr    o2   c4   0.400    112.000   0.000    0.000
ba    o2   c4   0.400    112.000   0.000    0.000
```

Mmpnbd.txt

The effective ionic radii at CN=6 from the Huheey text were used.

```
li     1.9600       0.0150
na1    2.6600       0.0150
k      3.4200       0.0150
rb     3.7200       0.0150
cs     4.1400       0.0150
mg2    2.2000       0.0150
ca2    2.7600       0.0150
sr     3.1200       0.0150
ba     3.4800       0.0150
```

Mmpstr.txt

```
li      o2      5.000   2.200   0.000   0.000
na1     o2      4.000   2.500   0.000   0.000
k       o2      4.000   2.800   0.000   0.000
rb      o2      3.000   3.000   0.000   0.000
cs      o2      2.000   3.150   0.000   0.000
mg2     o2      5.000   2.180   0.000   0.000
ca2     o2      5.000   2.600   0.000   0.000
sr      o2      5.000   2.700   0.000   0.000
ba      o2      4.000   2.820   0.000   0.000
```

Mmptor.txt

Two were defined for each of the metals. The same values were used for all cases. They are from the Hay paper.

```
M       o2      c4      c4      -1.100  0.880   0.200
M       o2      c4      h        0.000  0.000   0.060
```

16. The Acidity of Oxoacids

Most of the elements are found in nature not as free elements but in the form of ions. In the aqueous environment of the earth, the non-metals are most frequently found combined with oxygen in the form of various oxoanions, the conjugate bases of oxoacids. It will be convenient for this experiment consider the equilibrium written as the acid dissociation.

$$O_pE(OH)_q \ + \ H_2O \ \rightleftharpoons \ O_{p+1}E(OH)_{q-1}^- \ + \ H^+$$

   acid   conjugate base

The strength of an oxoacid is characterized by its pK_a, the negative logarithm of the acid ionization constants. If necessary, pK_a can be calculated from pK_b of the conjugate base using the relationship $pK_a = 14 - pK_b$.

The strength of an oxoacid can been attributed to several factors. For the series of acids such as HClO, HBrO and HIO, the strongest acid is HClO. This is related to the electronegativity of the central atom that produces an inductive effect on the hydroxyl group. The number of oxygen atoms surrounding the central atom is likewise important since the conjugate base can be stabilized through delocalization of the negative charge. Remember that the equilibrium state is determined by the species on both sides of the equation!

Various attempts have been made to correlate the strength of an oxoacid to some molecular parameter such as the electronegativity of the central atom, partial charges on the central element combined with a simple count of oxo and/or hydroxo groups, polarity of the OH bond, changes in the partial charge on the central atom that occur when ionization takes place, and many others.

In this experiment we will attempt to find a correlation between parameters that can be obtained from a computed model and the pK_a of a series of oxoacids. The calculation method you will use is one of the semi-empirical methods of quantum mechanics, PM3. This method has been parameterized for most of the main group elements.

When setting up the methods, you will be directed to the "options" box to set certain values. Charge is the overall charge on the molecule. Thus for the neutral acid the charge is zero but for the ions, the charge will be -1 or -2 depending on the number of hydrogen ions removed. Spin multiplicity is calculated as 2S + 1 where S is the number of unpaired electrons.

The halogen oxoacids that are known to exist in aqueous solution are shown below. The chemistry of these acids and their salts is very complicated however and in some cases pKa values are not available. These are designated with the asterisk. The pK_a values for perchloric and chloric acid are estimated from pK_b data. Bromine and iodine oxoacids are somewhat more complicated in aqueous solution, forming hydrated anions.

$HClO_4$	*$HBrO_4$	
$HClO_3$	*$HBrO_3$	HIO_3
$HClO_2$	*$HBrO_2$	*HOF
HOCl	HOBr	HOI

This will be a group project. During the lab period each student will model several acids and their conjugate bases starting with the seven halogen acids. You will use the accumulated class data to attempt to find correlation between the pK_a of the acid and some property that has been determined in the calculated structure. Several possibilities will be suggested but you should use your collective scientific knowledge to test other reasonable combinations. In each case state a reason why you choose the combination. You are encouraged to discuss these within the group.

Pre-Laboratory Assignment

Draw electron dot structures for the acids assigned to you by the instructor. Look up the pK_a in any available text book or reference work. You may find some slight differences in pK_a so be sure to record the source of information. Record the values of successive pK's where available. The CRC Handbook has a table of nomenclature for the oxoacids that may be helpful.

Computation

Draw the structure of the acid according to your Lewis dot formulas. Include any lone pairs on the central atom. Check Explicit Hydrogen on the Build menu and then modelbuild the structure. Double check to be sure the expected geometry is obtained.

Use the Display-Labels-Charge so charge will be shown as the computation proceeds. Setup a semi-empirical PM3 calculation with appropriate charge and multiplicity options. Complete a geometry optimization. Semi-empirical calculations require more time than the molecular mechanics calculations. Be patient! Save the file to your disk using the formula as the file name

Next you will do the drawing and calculation for the conjugate base. Remove a hydrogen from the acid and perform the optimization using the charge of –1 and multiplicity of 1 on the Options menu. Save the file under a new name.

Place the two figures on the same screen and prepare them for printing. If you already have the conjugate base on the screen merge it with the acid file using File-Merge.

To place the structures side by side, set Select to Molecules and double-click on one of the structures. Using the xy-tool R-drag the selected structure a convenient position. Rotate the structures if necessary so the charges on each atom are clearly visible.

Set File-Preferences-window to white. Then use Edit-Copy Image to obtain a printout of the workspace. This will have all of the charges displayed.

Obtain the geometric information indicated on the workspace; i.e. bond distances, angles about the central element. If the structure does not resemble your predicted geometry consult the instructor. Record the geometric information for each species (i.e. bond distances and angles) on the printout.

Correlation Studies

Your next task is to attempt to find a correlation between pK_a of the acid and some property or combination of properties of the system (i.e. acid and conjugate base)

Arrange the acids in order of increasing pK_a in a spreadsheet. Include the following information as a minimum.

- Full name, formula and pK_a of acid

- Partial Charge on central atom in acid and on central atom in conjugate base

- Charge on oxygen atom in acid before hydrogen was removed and on the same oxygen atom in the conjugate base

- Partial Charge on the hydrogen that is removed to form the base

Using pK_a as the dependent variable in each case, prepare graphs and do linear regressions for the following:

- pK_a vs. partial charge on central atom

- pK_a vs. partial charge on oxygen atom

- pK_a vs. partial charge on hydrogen

- pK_a vs. (differences in partial charge from acid to conjugate base)

- pK_a vs. (a ratio of partial charges of same element in acid and conjugate base) Why might this be a reasonable computation?

Test any other combinations you think are appropriate - for example, perhaps the polarity of the OH bond would correlate. How might this be estimated? Would you need additional information from the HyperChem program?

Obtain a print out showing the graphs and regressions you tried. Can you make any generalizations about the work thus far? Which values correlate the best? Considering the text book discussion of oxoacid strength, write a statement about why you think this is a reasonable prediction of acid strength.

Extension to Other Systems

Based on your hypothesis about the best correlation, the class should now extend the project to oxoacids of other non-metals. The table below shows acids for which pK_a values are available in the literature. In the case of di- and tri-protic acids successive equilibrium constants may be available.

Table 1 Oxoacids - Main Group Non-metals

Group 6	Group 5	Group 4
H_2O_2	HNO_3	H_2CO_3 (2)
H_2SO_4(2)	HNO_2	H_4SiO_4 (4)
H_2SO_3(2)	H_3PO_4(3)	H_2SiO_3 (2)
H_2SeO_4 (2)	H_3AsO_4 (3)	H_4GeO_4 (2)
H_2SeO_3(2)	$HAsO_2$	
H_2TeO_3 (2)		
H_6TeO_6		

Each of the above acids and their conjugate bases should be modeled in the same manner the halogen acids were treated. Remember to draw the Lewis structures by hand first. Check with each other and with the instructor if necessary to insure they are correct. There are double bonds in some of them. For simplicity, consider explicit double bonds as you model these rather than trying to consider resonance forms.

The information should be shared within the class and the class as a whole must determine the final results to answer the following questions.

1. Does the hypothesis you made on the basis of the halogen oxoacids hold for the other acids modeled?

2. Do any stand out as being quite different? Can you determine a pattern to any discrepancies?

3. Consider subsets of the total. Can you see any trend going across a period? Does the number of =O groups seem to make a difference?

4. Based on all of your work, try to draw a conclusion regarding the validity of your first hypothesis as a means of predicting acid strength (pK_a). If it is not valid, have you found a better predictor?

References

Cotton, F. Albert; Wilkinson, Geoffrey; Cotton, Frank A. *Advanced Inorganic Chemistry, 5th Edition*, Wiley: New York, 1988.

Jolly, W. L. *Modern Inorganic Chemistry*, McGraw-Hill: New York, 1991.

Meek, T. L. *J. Chem. Ed.*; **1992**, 69, 270-273.

Shriver, D. S.; Atkins, P. W.; Langford, C. H. *Inorganic Chemistry*, Freeman: San Francisco, 1994.

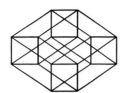

Chapter 3
Molecular Orbitals and Bonding

"Those who are not shocked when they first come across quantum theory cannot possibly have understood it."   Neils Bohr

The quantum mechanic description of matter in terms of wave functions and energy states is a difficult language to learn. Mastery of the mathematics and how results relate to experiment are not trivial matters! Yet, quantum mechanics is the tool that underlies much of computational chemistry. This chapter provides a few examples of student projects that could be used to explore very basic principles. The simulations in Exercises 17 could be used at the freshman level in courses where MO theory is included. Exercise 18 explores how to extract information about molecular orbitals from a HyperChem log file and how charge calculations are made using orbital electronic populations. The last three exercises are specific applications of how molecular orbitals information can assist us in understanding structure and reactivity.

17. Exploring the Formation of Molecular Orbitals - 1

This exercise is meant to give you a better understanding of the theoretical treatment of chemical bond formation known as Molecular Orbital Theory by visualizing the formation of molecular orbitals and preparing graphs of energy changes that occur as atoms move closer together.

Quantum mechanical methods involve solution of the Schrödinger equation that is frequently written in the compact form

$$\hat{H}\Psi = E\Psi$$

where $\hat{H}$ is the Hamiltonian operator, Ψ is a wave function and E is the eigenvalue for the energy. All of the quantum mechanical methods account for three kinds of electrostatic interactions that can occur when a molecule forms: electron-electron repulsion, internuclear repulsion and electron-nuclei attraction. The method to be used in this simulation is called MNDO, one of several methods in which an approximation called Neglect of Differential Overlap (NDO) is used to reduce the number of calculations. MNDO differs from some of the other semi-empirical methods in the way it deals with the repulsion that take place as the molecule forms. The nucleus and "core electrons" are parameterized in one term -- the core-repulsion term. MNDO deals with only the valence electrons in each atom of the molecule in calculating the attractive forces of electrons to the nuclei and electron-electron repulsion.

Simulation of Molecular Orbital Formation

A Tcl script is a set of commands that tells HyperChem to do certain tasks. The scripts will draw the molecule of interest, set the necessary parameters to do a MNDO calculation and proceed with the simulation. A log file will be saved for later analysis in one case. Use the mouse button to select a simulation. To begin the animation click on Script and the file called MO.tcl

This script file is shown at the end of the experiment.

H2 Sigma

The first script will show the formation of the sigma bonding MO as two hydrogen atoms move closer together (from 3.5Å to about 0.25Å). The contour plot showing the electron density computed from the wave function

$$\Psi(\sigma) \,=\, 1s_A \,+\, 1s_B$$

will be drawn as the atoms approach each other. The color is uniform (green) indicating that the sign of the wave function is positive. This script is also recording some of the computed values of energy that you will plot later. Repeat running the script as needed to try to get a "feeling" for the shape of the molecular orbitals. Sketch the approximate diagrams at the initial, middle and last diagrams during the simulation.

H2 Sigma*

The second script shows the formation of the sigma anti-bonding MO. The contour plot now shows the linear combination of atomic orbitals computer from the wave function

$$\Psi(\sigma*) \,=\, 1s_A \,-\, 1s_B$$

Note as you run this script, there are two colors: green indicates a positive value for the wave function and violet indicates negative. Watch what happens as the two atoms approach. Again, sketch the orbitals indicating the color in some way.

There is a node between the two atoms. This is a region of zero electron density. Since the node appears between the two molecules, the "glue" that holds the molecule together (i.e. the electrons) is missing hence this is called an "anti-bonding" orbital. This virtual orbitals are unoccupied in diatomic hydrogen since the bonding MO can accommodate the two electrons.

O2 Pi

This script simulates the formation of the highest occupied MO of oxygen, a bonding orbital formed by the overlap of two p orbitals approaching edge-on.

O2 Pi*

This script simulates the formation of an anti-bonding π molecular orbital.

The Molecular Orbital Diagrams

Obtain the optimum geometry for the hydrogen molecule. The calculation Setup settings were been done during the simulations and do not need to be repeated. Record the binding energy and bond distance for your report.

Move the hydrogen molecule to the left of the screen with the translate tool so you can see the plots as they are produced. Select Compute-Orbitals. Choose 3-D isosurface and in the Options box select Gouraud Shaded Surface. Then Click on each of the MO energy lines and Plot the orbital. Identify it as a bonding or anti-bonding case.

Plotting Energies

A number of the energy values calculated during the first simulation were saved in a file called H2.log. The definitions are as follows.

Isolated Atom Energy	Sum of the electronic energies for the individual unbound atoms. i.e. the attraction of the electrons for the nucleus in one atom.
Core-Core Interaction	Repulsion between the nuclei and inner electrons of one atom for the nuclei and inner electrons in the other atoms in the molecule.
Electronic Energy	Sum of attractions between valence electrons and cores plus valence electron repulsions within the molecule.
Total Energy	Core + Electronic
Binding Energy	Total Energy - Isolated Atom Energy

Obtain a printed copy of the log file. Open a spreadsheet and enter the values in a well-labeled table. The bond distances used in the simulation are recorded as "selection value." The others are self-explanatory. Include a computed column for Total Energy as defined above. Prepare a plot of each energy (core, electronic, total, binding) versus distance on a single carefully labeled graph.

What is the physical significance of the observation that the Core Energy increases as the bond distance decreases?

What is the physical significance of the observation that the Electronic Energy decreases as the bond distance decreases?

Using the graph, estimate the bond distance for the most stable molecule. I.e. at what distance is the total energy a minimum? Does this correspond to the bond distance in the optimized molecule?

According to Koopmans' Theorem, the energy of the HOMO should correspond to the first ionization energy of the molecule. Evaluate the calculated data in light of information you can find in the CRC Handbook or Lange's Handbook.   Show any unit conversions you do in making the comparisons.

	MNDO Calculation	Experimental
What is the energy of the HOMO?	_____	_____
What is the energy of the LUMO?	_____	_____
Record the bond-length for the molecule.	_____	_____

Reference

Atkins, P. *Physical Chemistry, 5ᵗʰ ed.* ; Freeman: New York, 1994.

```
## Tcl/tk script for Molecular orbital Simulation of
## sigma and pi bonding and anti-bonding orbitals.
##
##  GUI SET UP
##
label .l1 -text "MO Formation Simulation"
      button .b1 -text "H2 Sigma" -command sigma-h2
      button .b2 -text "H2 Sigma*" -command sigma*-h2
      button .b3 -text "O2 Pi" -command pi-O2
      button .b4 -text "O2 Pi*" -command pi*-O2
      button .b5 -text "Exit"  -command bye
pack .l1 .b1 .b2 .b3 .b4 .b5
##
## BUILDING OF DIATOMICS
##
proc build_H2 {} {hcExec "atom-labels symbol"
      hcExec "render-method sticks"
      hcExec "file-needs-saved no"
      hcExec "menu-file-new"
      hcExec "create-atom 1"
      hcExec "select-atom 1 1"
      hcExec "translate-selection 1 -.5 0"
      hcExec "create-atom 1"
      hcExec "set-bond 1 1 1 2 s"
      hcExec "select-atom 2 1"
}
proc build_O2 {} {hcExec "atom-labels symbol"
      hcExec "render-method sticks"
      hcExec "file-needs-saved no"
      hcExec "menu-file-new"
      hcExec "create-atom 8"
      hcExec "select-atom 1 1"
      hcExec "translate-selection 1 -.5 0"
      hcExec "create-atom 8"
      hcExec "set-bond 1 1 1 2 d"
      hcExec "select-atom 2 1"
}
##
## CALCULATIONS
##
proc set_up_calculation{} {hcExec "align-molecule primary x"
      hcExec "align-viewer y"
      hcExec "set-bond-length 3.5"
      hcExec "menu-display-scale-to-fit"
      hcExec "calculation-method semi-empirical"
      hcExec "semi-empirical-method mndo"
      hcExec "do-qm-calculation yes"
      hcExec "graph-orbital-selection-type orbital-number"
      hcExec "graph-data-type orbital"
      hcExec "graph-horizontal-grid-size 50"
      hcExec "graph-vertical-grid-size 50"
      hcExec "graph-contour-levels 10"
      hcExec "do-qm-graph yes"
}
```

```
proc do_calculation {} {
for {set i 3.5} {$i > 0 }  {set i [expr $i- 0.25]} {
        hcExec "set-bond-length ($i)"
        hcExec "do-single-point"
        hcExec "query-value selection-value"
        hcExec "query-value scf-atom-energy"
        hcExec "query-value scf-core-energy"
        hcExec "query-value scf-electronic-energy"
        hcExec "query-value scf-binding-energy"
        hcExec "pause-for 1"}
}
##
##   PROCEDURES ASSOCIATED WITH BUTTONS
##
proc sigma-h2 {} {
        build_H2
        hcExec "omsgs-to-file h2.log"
        hcExec "graph-orbital-offset 1"
        set_up_calculation
        do_calculation
}
proc sigma*-h2 {} {
        build_H2
        hcExec "graph-orbital-offset 2"
        set_up_calculation
        do_calculation
}
proc pi-O2 {} {
        build_O2
        hcExec "graph-orbital-offset 6"
        set_up_calculation
        do_calculation
}
proc pi*-O2 {} {
        build_O2
        hcExec "graph-orbital-offset 7"
        set_up_calculation
        do_calculation
}
proc bye {} {
        hcExec "exit-script"
        Exit
}
```

18. Exploring the Formation of Molecular Orbitals - 2

A HyperChem log file contains a great deal of information that is useful in understanding the chemistry of a system. In this exercise we will explore in more detail how some of those numbers are calculated. The example will use a simple molecule, hydrogen fluoride, optimized using MNDO. Portions of the log file with the QuantumPrintLevel = 1 are shown in these examples.

Method and Calculation Settings

```
Geometry optimization, SemiEmpirical, molecule = HF.
MNDO
PolakRibiere optimizer
Convergence limit = 0.0100000   Iteration limit = 50
Accelerate convergence = NO
Optimization algorithm = Polak-Ribiere
Criterion of RMS gradient = 0.1000 kcal/(A mol)Maximum
cycles = 30
RHF Calculation:
Singlet state calculation
Number of electrons = 8
Number of Double Occupied Levels = 4
Charge on the System = 0
Total Orbitals = 5
```

Eigenvalues (eV) and Eigenvectors

Mol. Orbital Symmetry:	1 1 SI	2 2 SI	3 1 PI	4 1 PI	5 3 SI
Eigenvalue	-43.16652	-17.77429	-14.82447	-14.82447	5.27487
S F 2	0.92088	-0.30924	-0.00000	0.00000	0.23737
Px F 2	-0.00000	-0.00000	-1.00000	0.00000	-0.00000
Py F 2	-0.13600	-0.82549	0.00000	0.00000	-0.54779
Pz F 2	0.00000	0.00000	0.00000	1.00000	-0.00000
S H 1	0.36535	0.47217	0.00000	-0.00000	-0.80223

This section contains information about the solutions of the Schrödinger equation. Here, five molecular orbitals are formed. Since HF has 8 valence electrons, four of them are occupied. The column below the orbital number shows the energy eigenvalue and the atomic orbitals that contribute to the molecular orbital. Molecular orbitals are linear combinations of atomic orbitals.

$$\Psi_{MO} \quad = \quad c_1\Psi_{AO} + c_2\,\Psi_{AO}$$

Molecular orbital 1 is thus formed from the fluorine 2s and $2p_y$ orbitals and the hydrogen 1s orbital.

$$\Psi_1 \quad = \quad 0.920\,\Psi\,(F_{2s}) - 0.136\Psi\,(F_{py}) + 0.365\Psi\,(H_{1s})$$

Write the equations for the other four orbitals. Include the energy and symmetry notation in the table.

Equation	Energy (eV)	Symmetry
$\Psi_1 = \quad 0.920\,\Psi\,(F_s) - 0.136\Psi\,(F_{py}) + 0.365\Psi\,(H_s)$	-43.16	
$\Psi_2 =$		
$\Psi_3 =$		
$\Psi_4 =$		
$\Psi_5 =$		

Use this information to construct a molecular orbital correlation diagram showing the atomic orbitals energy levels on the sides and the molecular orbital energy levels in the middle. Draw lines showing the atomic orbitals that contribute to each molecular orbital.

Calculating Charge

The square of the wave function is related to the probability of finding the electron in a particular volume element of the molecule. The charge distribution in a molecule is related to the wavefunction coefficients. Since the wavefunctions are normalized, the sum of the squares of the coefficients is 1. Using MO1 as the example, verify that

$$(0.92088)^2 + (-0.13600)^2 + (0.36535)^2 = 1$$

The charge density on a particular atom from all of the molecular orbitals is the sum of the squares of the coefficients of the occupied orbitals centered on that atom times the number of electrons in the molecular orbital. In this case all of the molecular orbitals are doubly occupied so the fluorine charge or the hydrogen charge can be calculated as follows.

	Fluorine		**Hydrogen**	
MO1	$2[(0.92088)^2 + (-0.13600)^2]$ = 1.73303		$2[(0.36535)^2]$ =	0.26696
MO2	$2[(-0.30924)^2 + (-0.82549)^2]$ = 1.55412		$2[(0.47216)^2]$ =	0.44587
MO3	$2[(-1.00000)^2]$ = 2.0000		$2[0.00000)^2]$ =	0.00000
MO4	$2[(-1.00000)^2]$ = 2.0000		$2[0.00000)^2]$ =	0.00000
MO5	not occupied			
Total Electron Density	= 7.28712		=	0.71287

The charge on each atom can now be calculated. It is the difference between the charge on the core and the electron density on the atom. This is the "charge" that appears when you select display-Labels-Charge in HyperChem. Fluorine in hydrogen fluoride shows a charge of –0.287.

Total electron density	=	-7.28712
Core Charge	=	+7
Net Charge	=	-0.2871

Try the calculation for oxygen to see if you get + 0.2871.

Atomic Orbital Electron Populations

This can be viewed as the fraction of the total electron charge that resides in each atomic orbital.

```
AO:    2   S   F      2   Px  F      2   Py  F      2   Pz  F      1   S   H
       1.887308        2.000000        1.399849        2.000000        0.712843
```

It is also calculated from the molecular orbital coefficients. For example, the population in the fluorine 2s orbital is

$$2 * [c_1^2 + c_2^2]^2 = 2[(0.92088)^2 = (0.30924)^2] = 1.88730$$

Try it for one of the other orbitals.

19. Molecular Orbitals: Ethene and Formaldehyde

In a later experiment we examine the π electron spectra of some organic molecules. In preparation, let's look at the simplest π bonding molecules to understand the orbitals that might be involved in electronic transitions.

An interesting way to look at the bonding in a molecule is to break the molecule into important fragments and see how the fragments interact. Hoffman employed this technique with outstanding success in examining the structures of organometallic complexes. This is one situation in which Extended Hückel Theory (EHT) shines since one can rigorously recast an Extended Hückel Hamiltonian into a basis set of fragment molecular orbitals to see just how much each one contributes to the molecular orbitals of the whole molecule. In addition, EHT includes overlap in its solution of the Hartree-Fock equations, which perhaps provides a better approximation of the bonding and anti-bonding interaction between fragment orbitals.

With HyperChem we can carry out a fragment molecular orbital analysis qualitatively by looking at the orbitals of CH_2, and then the orbitals of ethene.

To do the study, you need to carry out a number of molecular orbital calculations. Start first with a set of Extended Hückel calculations on the following molecules:

1. normal ethene

2. ethene twisted 45 degrees

3. ethene twisted 90 degrees

4. the carbene fragment (delete one end of ethene)

5. formaldehyde

Draw and modelbuild ethene. The HyperChem modelbuilder will draw ethene with the y-axis along the double bond, the z-axis perpendicular to the plan of the molecule and the x-axis in the plane of the molecule but perpendicular to the C=C bond. It will help analysis if each molecule is drawn in the same orientation. To construct the twisted forms, select the H-C-C-H torsion and Edit-Bond Torsion to set the new angle.

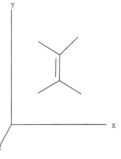

When you start the series of computations, turn on the log file to save all of the results. Set QuantumPrintLevel = 1 on the same screen as you name the log file. (In earlier versions of HyperChem modifying the chem.ini file did this.) You can enter a comment into the log file identifying the molecule and its conformation using Log Comments on the File menu.

The Carbene Fragment

Use a word processor to open up the log file and examine the orbital energies and coefficients of the carbene fragment. See if you can determine the orbitals that bond the hydrogen to the carbon.

Examine the EHT orbitals in CH_2. After the calculation is completed you can visualize the orbitals by selecting Orbitals from the compute menu. Check the Labels box to show the orbital occupancy and choose 3-D Isosurface for orbital plotting. Note that the symmetry designation of each orbital is given as a line is selected. Then use the log file output showing the atomic orbital contribution to each molecular orbital along with the plot of each orbital to see that:

- The lowest CH_2 orbital is a bonding combination of mostly carbon s orbitals with some hydrogen s orbital.

- The second CH_2 orbital is a bonding combination of the p_x carbon orbital with the hydrogen s orbital (best overlap and similar atomic energies.)

- The third orbital is essentially a p_y orbital pointing along the absent C=C bond. It bonds slightly with the hydrogens, but is mostly non-bonding in nature. It will form the σ orbital of the C=C bond in ethene.

- The fourth orbital is the non-bonded p_z orbital that will form the π orbital of ethene.

- The fifth orbital is the anti-bonding combination of the second orbital.

- The sixth orbital is the anti-bonding combination of the lowest energy orbital.

Plot or sketch the energy level diagram of the CH_2 molecular orbitals on each side of a piece of graph paper. Include the symmetry notation for each orbital.

Ethene Molecular Orbitals

In looking at the interaction between the two fragments, remember that there is always a bonding/anti-bonding combination formed when any two orbitals interact. With three interacting orbitals, the combination is often a bonding, a non-bonding and an anti-bonding set.

Next, examine the orbitals of ethene using EHT and determine from which orbitals of the CH_2 fragment each of the MO's of ethene arise. Put the MO energies of ethene in the center of the graph paper. Using the log file information, draw correlation lines from the CH_2 orbitals to the ethene orbitals. Which of the MO's are essentially non-bonding between the two CH_2 fragments and which are bonding the two carbons together? For example, which ethene orbitals arises from the overlap of orbitals which are primarily $C1(p_y)$- $C2(p_y)$, or $C1(p_z)$- $C2(p_z)$?

Frontier Orbital Interaction as a Function of Twist Angle

In this part of the exercise you will plot the orbital energies of a CH_2 fragment along with the energies of the orbitals in ethene at 0, 45 and 90 degrees. You will see that the lowest two molecular orbitals in ethene show virtually no change in energy, while there is a marked change in the orbital energies of those orbitals between about –8 and –17 eV. Remember that the fragment molecular energies are unchanged no matter what the orientation. Compare the charts and notice which orbital interactions are most affected. There are a number of ways to look at the change in MO energies but the simplest is to realize the following.

- The $p\pi$ and pseudo-$p\pi$ orbitals are far apart in energy and they don't overlap very well. The pseudo-pi orbitals on the carbene involve a good mix of carbon p_x and hydrogen 1s, and so lie behind carbon, hence the splitting of bonding and anti-bonding for the pseudo-pi orbitals in twisted ethene is much less than that for the $p\pi$ orbitals.

- When the molecule is twisted, the interaction $p\pi$–$p\pi$ and pseudo-pi–pseudo-pi are zero, so the only interacting is the small $p\pi$ - pseudo-pi interaction (two of them). Do you see the slight lowering of the pseudo π orbital energy and the slight rising of the $p\pi$ orbital energy?

Put electrons in the orbitals and look at the net bonding.

Formaldehyde

Once more do an EHT calculation with a CH_2 fragment attached to an oxygen atom to make formaldehyde. The oxygen fragment orbitals are just the atomic orbitals with $E(O_{2p}) = -14.8$ eV and $E(O_{2s}) = -32.3$ eV.

In this case, notice the pi and sigma bonds between the p orbitals on the oxygen and the $p\pi$ and $p\sigma$ fragment MO's on the CH_2 fragment. The two bonding orbital energies are bracketed, top and bottom, by the energies of the bonding/anti-bonding interaction of the pseudo-pi orbitals on the CH_2 fragment (the one bonding the carbon and two hydrogens, so that the topmost filled orbital is essentially a non-bonding orbital.

Finally, redo planar ethene and formaldehyde calculations using a log file with ZINDO/S and PM3 calculations. Optimize the geometry of each molecule first using PM3. Compare the molecular orbitals in each case with the EHT orbitals to be certain you know which are which in case the ordering is slightly different.

20. Walsh Diagrams for H_2X Molecules

Walsh diagrams are useful in predicting molecular geometry. They correlate energy changes of molecular orbitals between a reference geometry, frequently of high symmetry, and a deformed structure of lower symmetry.

For this exercise we will consider two simple molecules: BeH_2 and H_2O to see how it works. A sample Excel spreadsheet and macro to extract the data is given.

H_2O

Set up the system for a semi-empirical calculation. Draw and modelbuild the water molecule. Select the three atoms and set the bond angle to 180° using the Edit-Set bond Angle option. Open a log file at QuantumPrintLevel = 1 and do a single point calculation. Repeat at 10° intervals down to 80°. (A spreadsheet macro can be used to automate this process. See below).

Extract the orbital energy and the symmetry notation for each of the occupied orbitals from the log file. The log file also contains the orbital coefficients that will be needed to answer some of the questions below. The symmetry classification for the 180° form uses the abbreviations SIG, SIU, and PIU for σ_g, σ_u and π_u respectively. For the angular molecules this classification is no longer valid since there is no axis of symmetry. Symmetry relationships in polyatomic molecules are labeled a_1, b_2 etc.

Prepare a correlation diagram showing energy as a function of angle for the occupied orbitals. Include the symmetry notation on the end points of each line. Observe the following and answer the questions.

$1a_1$: The lowest energy orbital is labeled $1a_1$. Which atomic orbitals overlap to form this molecular orbital? How does this contribution change as the angle changes?

$1b_2$: How does the correlation energy change as the bond angle changes?

$2a_1$: The largest change is observed for this level. Identify the orbital contribution in the 90° and the 180° forms. Is it reasonable to expect a larger change?

$1b_1$: Note that this is a non-bonding (p_z) orbital in all of the structures and that its energy does not change.

Overall, at what angle is the most stable arrangement of electrons possible?

Remember that the core-core interaction also plays an important role in determining the overall stability of the molecule.

BeH$_2$

Repeat the exercise with BeH$_2$ to determine the most likely geometry of this molecule. Prepare a Walsh Diagram showing the energy of the occupied orbitals as the angle changes.

Excel Spreadsheet and Macro

To use the macro, you must select and name the H-E-H angle, Angle. Set up a worksheet with angles from 90-180 degrees in column A. The macro will report the components shown.

Angle	Core-Core Energy	Electronic Energy	Binding Energy	Orbital Energy					
				-4	-3	-2	-1	0	1
90									
95									
Etc.									

Select the 90-degree cell of the spreadsheet before invoking the macro. After the macro has run it will be necessary to convert the SCF-orbitals energy array data to individual cells. To do this, highlight the data in column E. Use the Data menu to select "text to columns." Follow the directions indicating that a semicolon is used as a separator. After the data is parsed, it will be necessary to strip off the leading and ending brackets and to set the type to numeric.

References

Atkins, P. *Physical Chemistry, 5th ed.*; Freeman: San Francisco, 1994.

Huheey, J. E.; Keiter, E. A.; Keiter, R. L. *Inorganic Chemistry 4th ed.*; HarperCollins, New York 1993.

Control-R	Compute.Results
Channel	=OpenFile()
	=IF(ISERROR(Channel))
	=RETURN()
	=END.IF()
	=EXECUTE(Channel,"[query-response-has-tag(no)]")
	=EXECUTE(Channel,"[file-format(hin)]")
	=WHILE(NOT(ISBLANK(SELECTION())))
	=EXECUTE(Channel,"[select-name Angle]")
	=EXECUTE(Channel,"[set-bond-angle("&SELECTION()&")]")
	=EXECUTE(Channel,"[select-none]")
	=EXECUTE(Channel,"[do-single-point]")
	=FORMULA.ARRAY(REQUEST(Channel,"scf-core-energy"),"rc[1]")
	=FORMULA.ARRAY(REQUEST(Channel,"scf-electronic-energy"),"rc[2]")
	=FORMULA.ARRAY(REQUEST(Channel,"scf-binding-energy"),"rc[3]")
	=FORMULA.ARRAY(REQUEST(Channel,"scf-orbital-energy"),"rc[4]")
	=SELECT("r[1]c")
	=NEXT()
	=TERMINATE(Channel)
	=RETURN()
	OpenFlle
NewChan	=INITIATE("HyperChem","System")
	=IF(ISERROR(NewChan))
	= IF(ISERROR(EXEC("c:\Hyper5\PROGRAM\chem.exe",1)))
	=RETURN(NewChan)

	=END.IF()
	=RETURN(INITIATE("HyperChem","System"))
	=END.IF()
	=RETURN(NewChan)
	=END.IF()

21. The Jahn-Teller Effect

Octahedral transition metal complexes such as MX_6^z are sometimes found to be highly symmetric. However, distortions from pure O_h symmetry are known even with six identical ligands. The Jahn-Teller distortion occurs when two ligands that are trans to each other move either closer to or farther away from the metal than the other four ligands. In both cases the symmetry is lowered from O_h to D_{4h} so the energy of the d orbitals changes. Assuming the change takes place on the z-axis, elongation of the M-L bond lowers the energy of the d_{xz}, the d_{yz} and the d_{z2} orbitals. Compression lowers the energy of the d_{xy} and the d_{x2-y2} orbitals.

In this exercise we will examine the relationship of this kind of distortion to the occupancy of the metal d orbitals. Specifically, we will investigate how the binding energy of the complex changes as the symmetry changes from O_h to D_{4h} by elongation or compression on the z-axis.

MnF_6^{3-}

Draw the expected orbital splitting and occupancy for the d orbitals in an octahedral field. This is a high-spin d^4 complex. How many unpaired electrons does it have? Which orbitals are occupied?

Draw and modelbuild the structure. Measure the Mn-F bond distance and make a note of it in the table. We will explore distortions in a range of about 1.2-3.0 Å. Set the two trans axial bonds to the first value in the table.

Set up a semi-empirical ZINDO/1 calculation. Use the Options menu to set the charge to –3 and the multiplicity to a value appropriate for the number of unpaired electrons. Remember multiplicity is 2S + 1 where S is the sum of the spin (½) for each unpaired electron.

Do a single point ZINDO/1 calculation and record the binding energy from the status line. Change the axial bond lengths to the next value and repeat the single-point calculation. When finished, plot the binding energy as a function of the parameter X to determine the "best" structure. What is the most favorable bond length for the axial groups?

When finished, optimize the structure to determine if the full calculation gives the same result.

NiF_6^{3-}

The nickel complex is a low-spin d^7 case. Repeat the calculations for this complex. Don't forget to change the multiplicity.

Axial Lengths (Å)	MnF_6^{3-} Energy (kcal/mol)	NiF_6^{3-} Energy (kcal/mol)
1.50		
1.55		
1.60		
1.65		
1.70		
1.75		
1.80		
1.85		
1.90		
1.95		
2.00		
2.05		
2.10		
2.15		
2.20		
2.25		
2.30		
2.35		
2.40		
2.45		
2.50		

Discuss the results in terms of the orbital occupancy. How many electrons are stabilized by changes in the geometry? Why is elongation favored in one case while compression is favored in the other?

A Tcl/Tk script to simplify this exercise is shown on the next page. It will draw and modelbuild the structures. During the calculation a pause will allow you to write down the energy from the status line starting from the first table value.

References

Yoshida, S.; Sakaki, S.; Kobayashi, H. *Electronic Processes in Catalysis;* VCH: Basel, 1994, pp. 775-76.

Nicke, G; Reinhold, J. *J. Mol. Str. (Theochem.)*; **1985**, 124, 88.

Reinen, D.; Friebel, C. *Struct. Bonding(Berlin)*; **1979,** 37, 1.

```
# Tcl/tk script for Investigating the Jahn-Teller Effect
## in Octahedral transition metal complexes.
##
##   GUI SET UP
##
label .l1 -text "Jahn-Teller Effect"
label .l2 -text "Build a Molecule"
  button .b1 -text "(NiF6)3-" -command build_Ni
  button .b2 -text "(MnF6)3-" -command build_Mn
  button .b3 -text "Calculate the energies!" -width 20 -command
distort
  button .b4 -text "Exit"  -command bye
pack .l1 .l2 .b1 .b2 .b3 .b4
####
##   PROCEDURES ASSOCIATED WITH BUTTONS
##   Building of Nickel complex
##
proc build_Ni {} {hcExec "atom-labels symbol"
      hcExec "render-method sticks"
      hcExec "file-needs-saved no"
      hcExec "menu-file-new"
      hcExec "create-atom 28"
      for {set i 1} {$i <= 6}  {incr i} {
            hcExec "create-atom 9"
            hcExec "set-bond 1 1 1 2 s"
            hcExec "menu-build-model-build"
      }
      hcExec "rotate-viewer y 10"
      hcExec "rotate-viewer x 10"
      set_up_method
      hcExec "multiplicity 2"
}
##   Buliding of Manganese complex
##
proc build_Mn {} {hcExec "atom-labels symbol"
      hcExec "render-method sticks"
      hcExec "file-needs-saved no"
      hcExec "menu-file-new"
      hcExec "create-atom 25"
      for {set i 1} {$i <= 6}  {incr i} {
            hcExec "create-atom 9"
            hcExec "set-bond 1 1 1 2 s"
            hcExec "menu-build-model-build"
      }
      hcExec "rotate-viewer y 10"
      hcExec "rotate-viewer x 10"
      set_up_method
      hcExec "multiplicity 5"
}
```

```
##
## CALCULATIONS
##
proc set_up_method {} {
      hcExec "calculation-method semi-empirical"
      hcExec "semi-empirical-method zindo1"
      hcExec "quantum-total-charge -3"
}
proc distort {} {
      for {set length 1.5} {$length <= 2.5}  {set length [expr
$length + 0.05 ]} {
            hcExec "select-atom 1 1"
            hcExec "select-atom 2 1"
            hcExec "set-bond-length $length"
            hcExec "select-none"
            hcExec "select-atom 1 1"
            hcExec "select-atom 5 1"
            hcExec "set-bond-length $length"
            hcExec "select-none"
            hcExec "menu-display-scale-to-fit"
            hcExec "do-qm-isosurface false"
            hcExec "do-single-point"
            hcExec "pause-for 2"
            set energy($length)  [hcQuery "scf-binding-energy"]
      }
}
proc bye {} {
      hcExec "exit-script"
      Exit
}
```

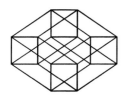

Chapter 4
Conformational Analysis

Molecules can rotate about single bonds. This simple statement has enormous implications in chemistry. Molecules are flexible and may adopt strikingly different shapes without breaking or making any bonds. These arrangements called conformations are separated from each other by energy differences that can sometimes be overcome by thermal energy. The barriers between other arrangements can be significant. Conformational analysis is the study of the relative energies (stability) of the conformation of a given molecule.

Particularly important conformation studies are those involving polypeptides. The linear, one-dimensional amino acid sequences are translated into three-dimensional protein conformations with immense variety of structure and of function. From physically tough fibrous proteins such as hair and nails that are insoluble in water to the spherical or globular shapes that characterize water soluble enzymes or transport proteins, conformation makes a difference!

22. Small Molecule Conformational Analysis by Hand

In order to find more than one conformational isomer of a molecule with bonds that can be rotated, it is necessary to go beyond the method of geometry optimization.

Rotation about a single bond in a molecule leads to a potential energy surface that has more than one minimum. Each minimum represents a conformational isomer. When geometry optimization is started, the nearest minimum will be reached as the calculation proceeds. Thus if a molecule has a starting geometry represented by point A, convergence will be reached when the structure reaches point B, the nearest "local" minimum. If the starting geometry is C, the "global" minimum energy represented by point D will be reached on optimization. Energy minimization algorithms go down, not up, potential energy surfaces. They will not cross energy barriers. In order to locate conformational isomers, we must cross the barriers by other methods. In this exercise, you will find stable conformation and estimate the height of the barriers to rotation for monosubstituted methane and benzene.

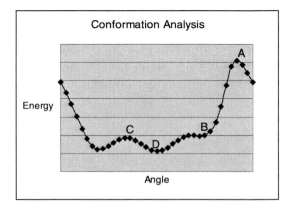

Optimizing Target Structures by "Trial and Error"

In some cases stable conformers of a molecule can be found by using chemical common sense. We know that the low energy structures of a molecule will not be those that give rise to strong repulsive forces between non-bonded atoms. To find structures corresponding to energy minima, we choose values of torsion angles that minimize repulsion (i.e., maximize the distances) between non-bonded pairs of atoms, then optimize the geometry with molecular mechanics.

Select a molecule from the table below. Build it and use the modelbuilder to convert it to a three dimensional structure. Optimize the geometry using MM+. Use the rotation tools to find a view looking along the specified rotation angles ("the Neumann projection") and note possible stable values of the rotation angle. Record these estimated torsion angles in the table.

Set the value of the selected torsion angle to generate the target structure. Do this by selecting the four atoms and invoking Edit-Set Torsion Angle. Deselect the atoms and perform the geometry optimization on this starting structure. Finally measure the record the value of the rotation angle for the optimized structure.

Carefully note any deviations of the results from your expectations. Then go on to the next molecule.

Molecule	Torsion Angle	Minimum 1		Minimum 2		Minimum 3	
		Est	Actual	Est	Actual	Est	Actual
CH_3-CH_3	H-C-C-H						
CH_3-CHO	H-C-C-H						
CH_3-OH	H-C-O-H						
CH_3-NH_2	H-C-N-H						
C_6H_5-CHO	C=C-C-H						
C_6H_5-OH	C=C-O-H						
C_6H_5-NO_2	C=C-N=O						

For some molecular species it is not easy to guess the geometry of the most stable conformers. A quick calculation of the energy as the torsion angle is varied incrementally leads to identification of the target structures for later optimization.

Use this method on one or more of the molecules from the previous table. Build and optimize the structure. Set the torsion angle to zero and do a single point energy calculation. Vary the angle from 0° to 180° in increments of 15° to 30°. Tabulate and graph these single point torsion energies and identify the structures corresponding to energy minima. Optimize them; record the optimized energy and torsion angle. These optimized structures are the stable conformers.

Angle	Single Point Energy (kcal/mol)	Optimized Energy (kcal/mol)	Optimized Angle
20	4.56		
40	3.09		
60	2.36	0.816	60
80	3.09		
100	4.56		

While this can be done very easily for any one molecule, it is tedious. A procedure for running the calculations from an Excel spreadsheet is given in the next exercise.

23. Small Molecule Conformation Analysis Using Macros

An approximate quantitative exploration of the potential energy for rotation about a single dihedral angle is easy to obtain and is useful in predicting stable conformations for more complex structures. In this lab you will modify an existing macro to produce a "dihedral driver" that will generate a table of single point energies as a function of dihedral angle. The calculations are run from Microsoft Excel and can be tailored to individual user preferences.

For each of the molecules studied, you will determine the number of energy minima and the approximate energy barrier to rotation. From calculations like these you will be able to make reasonable predictions of stable conformations of more complex structures.

Use HyperChem to build ethane. After optimizing the structure with MM+, select and name the H-C-C-H dihedral angle. Selecting the four atoms and invoking Select-Name Selection menu does this. We've called it "yourname" in the example below. Deselect the angle once it is named.

Open Excel and the file called C:/Hyper5/Scripts/Plot.xlm. (The path may vary depending on your version of HyperChem and local installation conventions.) Find the line that reads

```
=EXECUTE(Channel,"[openfile(c:\hyper5\samples\aromatic\"&SELECTION()&"
.hin)][do-single-point]")
```

Insert the following four lines after that line and then delete it.

```
=EXECUTE(Channel,"[set-name yourname]")
```
```
=EXECUTE(Channel,"[set-bond-torsion(&SELECTION()&")]")
```
```
=EXECUTE(Channel,"[select-none]")
```
```
=EXECUTE(Channel,"[do-single-point]")
```

Be sure to use your selection name for the dihedral angle where the macro says "yourname." You can also remove the lines that request the component energies (stretch, bend, torsion, non-bonded) since we are only looking at the total energy in this exercise. The full macro is shown at the end of this exercise. **Save this macro giving it a new name.**

Open a new worksheet file in Excel. The macro will read values of the dihedral angle from the first column in the sheet and report the "Total

Energy" in the next column. You can do the calculation for as many angles as you wish. Set up your worksheet so that it looks like this.

Sample Excel Worksheet

Dihedral Angle	Total Energy
0	
30	
60	
90	
etc.	

To run the calculation, use the mouse to highlight (activate) the worksheet cell containing the first value for the angle. Then under the Excel tools menu, choose Macro. In the dialog box, choose your recently created macro which is listed as "Macroname.xlm!Compute.Results". Then click run. The data will appear in the worksheet as values are generated.

To do a quantum mechanical calculation instead of molecular mechanics, go to HyperChem window and under Setup, choose semi-empirical. Select the method you want to use. Return to Excel as before to run the calculation.

Results

Tabulate data for the compound listed below. In addition to the tabulation of the dihedral energies (and associated graphs) in Microsoft Excel, it is useful to summarize the results in a form that is convenient for comparison.

Location (dihedral angle) of Energy Minima

Compound	Dihedral	Conformer 1	Conformer 2	Conformer 3
H_2O_2	H-O-O-H			
CH_3OH	H-C-O-H			
CH_3CHO	H-C-C=O			
CH_3CH_3	H-C-C-H			
CH_3CH_2Cl	H-C-C-Cl			
$CH_3CH_2CH_3$	H-C-C-C			

Relative MM+ Energy of Stable Conformers

Compound	Dihedral	Conformer 1	Conformer 2	Conformer 3
H_2O_2	H-O-O-H			
CH_3OH	H-C-O-H			
CH_3CHO	H-C-C=O			
CH_3CH_3	H-C-C-H			
CH_3CH_2Cl	H-C-C-Cl			
$CH_3CH_2CH_3$	H-C-C-C			

Excel Macro

Control-R	Compute.Results
	Compute.Results
Channel	=OpenFile()
	=IF(ISERROR(Channel))
	=RETURN()
	=END.IF()
	=EXECUTE(Channel,"[query-response-has-tag(no)]")
	=EXECUTE(Channel,"[file-format(hin)]")
	=WHILE(NOT(ISBLANK(SELECTION())))
	=EXECUTE(Channel,"[select-name yourname]")
	=EXECUTE(Channel,"[set-bond-torsion("&SELECTION()&")]")
	=EXECUTE(Channel,"[select-none]")
	=EXECUTE(Channel,"[do-single-point]")
	=FORMULA.ARRAY(REQUEST(Channel,"total-energy"),"rc[1]")
	=SELECT("r[1]c")
	=NEXT()
	=TERMINATE(Channel)
	=RETURN()
	OpenFile
NewChan	=INITIATE("HyperChem","System")
	=IF(ISERROR(NewChan))
	=IF(ISERROR(EXEC("c:\Hyper5\PROGRAM\chem.exe",1)))
	=RETURN(NewChan)
	=END.IF()
	=RETURN(INITIATE("HyperChem","System"))
	=END.IF()
	=RETURN(NewChan)
	=END.IF()

24. Torsion Barriers: Methyl and Phenyl

It is often useful to know the height of a rotational barrier since its magnitude, relative to the thermal energy at a given temperature, determines the probability of torsional transitions at that temperature. Experimental values for rotational barriers are useful in evaluating various methods of barrier heights.

In this exercise we introduce the technique of restrained optimization and apply it to the estimation of energy barriers to rotation. The technique consists of adding a restraining force to the calculation to fix the relative positions of two or more atoms, followed by geometry optimization of the rest of the molecule. Because of the constraint, this type of calculation takes longer than a typical optimization. The hope is that the energy obtained will correspond more closely than the single point energy to that of a real physical system.

You can use the experimental barriers to rotation that are given for comparison.

Single Point Estimate

Build the molecule(s) of interest. Optimize the structure to find the nearest stable conformer. If you have access to Microsoft Excel, use the dihedral driver macro described in the previous exercise to locate the torsional maxima. If not, do single point calculations for a range of dihedral angles in the vicinity of the maximum. When you are satisfied that you have located the top of the barrier, note the value of the angle (θ_{max}) and the associated single point energy. The difference between this value and the energy of the stable conformer is a first (crude) estimate of the barrier height. Note that the energy calculation may be done with molecular mechanics, semi-empirical or (the slowest!) *ab initio* methods. A comparison of these methods is also of interest.

Constrained Optimization Estimate

A better estimation is obtained by holding this angle fixed and optimizing the rest of the structure. To do a constrained optimization, first select the four atoms of the dihedral angle of interest and name that selection, e.g. "tor1." With "tor1" selected, go to the build menu, choose Set Bond Torsion, and enter the value of θ_{max}. Under Setup, choose Set Restraints. In the Restraints dialog box, choose "tor1" as the item to be restrained. Check that its value is "calculated" and correct. Increase the Force constant to a very large number, around 10^5, so that the angle is rigidly fixed at the desired value. With the restraint in place, deselect "tor1" and optimize the geometry of the molecule. This may take a larger number of iterations. Be sure that the calculation has converged before proceeding to the next step.

When you are satisfied that you have optimized the structure, save it. Go back to the Set Restraints under Setup and use the delete button to remove the restraint. Do a Single-Point energy calculation to calculate the energy (without any contribution from the restraining term) of the molecule in this geometry. Record this value.

This last value, minus the energy at the bottom of the hill, is the "constrained optimization" estimate of the energy barrier to rotation. We've allowed the rest of the molecule to "relax" while holding the torsion angle fixed. This generally leads to a significant improvement over the single point estimate.

Torsional barriers for a wide selection of small molecules are shown in the table on the next page.

References

Lowe, J. P., In *Progress in Physical Organic Chemistry*; Streitwieser, A and Taft, R. W., Eds.; Wiley Interscience: New York, 1968; Vol. 6, p 1.

Clark, M.; Cramer, R. D.; van Opdenbosch, N. *J. Comp. Chem.* 1989, 10(8), pp 9982-1012.

Molecule	Experimental Barrier (kcal/mol)	Single Point Estimate Barrier (kcal/mol)	Constrained and Optimized Barrier (kcal/mol)
Ethane	2.9		
Fluoroethane	3.3		
Chloroethane	3.7		
Bromoethane	3.7		
Iodoethane	3.2		
Methanol	1.1		
Acetaldehyde	1.2		
Methylamine	2.0		
Dimethylamine	3.6		
Benzaldehyde	4.9, 4.7		
Phenol	3.3, 3.4		
Nitrobenzene	2.9		
Propane	3.4		
Butane CH_3-CC-CH_3 eclipsed			
Butane CH_3-CC-H eclipsed	3.4		

23. Small Molecule Conformation Analysis Using Macros

Isobutane	3.9		
Neopentane	4.7		
Methylsilane	1.7		
Dimethyl ether	2.7		

24. The "Peptide Bond" in N-methylacetamide

The conformation of the peptide bond is obviously of great interest to biochemists. In this exercise we will investigate N-methylacetamide (NMA), an organic molecule that provides a simple model for the structure and conformational characteristics of the peptide bond. The strong preference for the trans conformation and the sizeable barrier to rotation characteristic of the peptide bond can be studied using molecular mechanics or using a quantum mechanical method. We will use OPLS, a force field developed for biomolecules, and a semi-empirical method (PM3) to investigate the energetics.

cis-NMA   trans-NMA

Build and optimize the trans- and cis- conformers of N-methylacetamide using the OPLS molecular mechanics force field. Record the energy from the status line and the various angles and bond lengths for each conformation in the tables on the next page. Calculate the energy difference between the two conformers.

Change the Setup to semi-empirical and choose PM3 (or AM1). Optimize the two structures and again determine the energy and the geometric information indicated.

Note any significant differences in geometry. With the semi-empirical calculation, information on the dipole moment and charge distribution is available as well.

Obtain the dipole moment from a .log file or by using the script:

query-value dipole-moment

The charge density can be displayed using Display-Labels-Charge.

Cis-trans Energy and Dipole Moment Differences

	OPLS (kcal/mol)	PM3 energy (kcal/mol)	Experimental (kcal/mol)	Dipole Moment (Debyes)	Experimental Dipole Moment
cis				4.21	
trans				4.04	
cis – trans			2.07	0.17	

Charge Distribution

	Carbonyl Carbon	Carbonyl Oxygen	Peptide Nitrogen
cis			
trans			

Geometric Information

	OPLS (Å)	PM3 (Å)	Experimental (Å)
cis-bond lengths			
N-CH$_3$			1.445
N-CO			1.357
C=O			1.200
trans- bond lengths			
N-CH$_3$			1.447
N-CO			1.353
C=O			1.200
cis- bond angles			
H-N-CH$_3$			114.0
H-N-CO			127.4
trans- bond angles			
H-N-CH$_3$			121.5
H-N-CO			119.4
Torsion			
cis H-N-C=O			
trans H-N-C=O			

With the above information and the charge distribution information, rationalize the results of the structure optimizations and the cis-trans energy differences.

Reference

Jorgensen, W. L.; Gao, J. *J. Amer. Chem. Soc.* **1988**, 110, 4212-4216.

26. Stable Conformers of the Alanine Dipeptide

The alanine dipeptide used in this exercise is a small unit that contains many structural features in common with the protein backbone. In it, the amino acid alanine is blocked with an acetyl group and a methyl amide group. Among the protein features it contains are flexible ϕ and ψ dihedral angles, two amide peptide bonds whose NH and CO groups are capable of participating in hydrogen bonding, and a methyl group attached to the α carbon, representative of an amino side chain. The angle of rotation about the C_α-N bond is called the ϕ (phi) angle. The ψ (psi) angle designates the rotation about the C_α-C bond. Theoretically free rotation can occur about these single bonds but if the R group (here a H_3C_β methyl) is large, rotation can be hindered. Further, when these two angles rotate in relation to each other, two H atoms (or O atoms) of the peptide bonds could overlap hindering free rotation. The study of stable conformations is of great interest in investigating the helical structure of proteins.

Good quality calculations have been done on the isolated molecule and these are useful as benchmarks for testing the performance of force fields on model "proteins." You will find the energies of stable conformers of the alanine dipeptide using three force fields. MM+ is an "all-purpose" force field while the Amber and OPLS force fields that were developed specifically for biomolecules.

In this exercise you will explore several questions. First, do all of the force fields optimize to the same structure? We will investigate this using the overlay feature of HyperChem. For a given force field, how well do the relative energies of conformers compare to the values in the table that were reported by Tobias and Brooks using the CHARMM force field?

Modelbuild and save the alanine dipeptide in each of the three conformers. Use Edit-Set Bond Torsion to set the dihedral angles, ϕ and ψ, to those reported by Tobias and Brooks as local minima. Choose the MM+ force field and optimize each structure. Save each with a unique name. Measure the two dihedral angles in the optimized structure as well as its energy. Compute the energies of the C_5 and C_{7ax} conformers relative to C_{7eq} and enter the values in the table. Repeat for each force field using different names as you save each structure.

Visual Comparison

The structures can be compared visually by overlaying portions. To compare for example, conformation 1 optimized with MM+ to conformation 1 optimized with Amber do the following to overlay important features.

Orient the first structure in the workspace so the feature you wish to look at is conveniently positioned. (E.g. H-C_α-N) Under the Display menu, choose Color and pick a color. This will enable you to distinguish conformers once they are overlaid. Then use File-Merge to add the second structure to the workspace.

Select three atoms of interest in structure 1 (H-C_α-N) followed by the three corresponding atoms in structure 2. The order of selection is important. HyperChem will attempt to match the first atom selected in molecule 1 with the first selected in molecule 2 and so on. On the Display menu choose Overlay. De-select atoms by L-clicking in the workspace.

Dihedral Angle Comparison

How do the methods tested compare? Were the local minima found using CHARRM also minima in the other methods?

See the HyperChem "Computational Chemistry" manual for additional information about the available force fields.

Ramachandran Plot

Ramachandran plots show energy as a function of ϕ and ψ. An Excel macro called PHIPSI.XLM to gather such data is distributed with ChemPlus or can be downloaded from the Hypercube home page. [http://www.hyper.com/] You will need to apply names to two torsional angles in your structure with Select-Name Selection before starting this macro. There are several options for restrained minimization, etc.

Reference

Tobias, D. J.; Brooks III, C. L. *J. Phys. Chem.* **1992**, 96, 3863-3870.

Conformation	Method	ϕ	ψ	Energy (kcal/mol)	Local minimum?
1	CHARMM	- 77.5	89.9	0	yes
2	CHARMM	-134.8	145.9	1.78	yes
3	CHARMM	60.6	-72.4	2.00	yes
1	MM+				
2	MM+				
3	MM+				
1	Amber				
2	Amber				
3	Amber				

27. The Inversion Barrier in Ammonia and Aniline

In this exercise you will look at the pyramidal shape of nitrogen compounds at two different levels of investigation. The inversion barrier at nitrogen can be estimated by comparing the energy of a pyramidal form with that of planar nitrogen.

This first investigation is taken from the HyperChem 4.5 manual as an interesting example of an *ab initio* application. Calculating the ammonia inversion barrier requires a moderately good basis set and a calculation of the molecular energy at its optimized pyramidal geometry and in an optimized planar form.

The Pyramidal Form

Use the modelbuilder to construct NH_3. From the display menu, select labels and choose Basis Set. Initially each element should indicate none.

Use the setup menu to select the *ab initio* 3-21G method. L-click on Apply Basis Set. Make the following selections from the submenus. Under Options set the SCF convergence to 0.01 with an interation limit of 50.

In the workspace, select the nitrogen atom. Under Advanced Options choose 6 d orbitals. Under Extra Basis Functions, choose D with an exponent of 1.0. Finally L-click Apply Basis Functions. De-select the nitrogen by R-clicking in the workspace. Your workspace should now contain the following image.

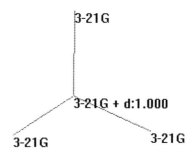

Do a geometry optimization using Polock-Ribiere with RMS = 0.1. Record the energy and the H-N-H angle in the table below.

The Planar Form

Select the nitrogen and then each of the three hydrogen atoms. HyperChem will note that this is an improper torsion angle. Give the selection a name, e.g., improper.

Under the Setup menu, choose restraints, move 4-improper to the restraint list. Set the restraint to 180 and set the force at 500.

The set up of the *ab initio* calculation is still in effect so you can optimize the geometry using the restrained torsion without changing the settings. This should give the optimized planar structure. To compare the energy with that of the pyramidal structure, you will need to remove the restraint and carry out a single point energy calculation with MP2 option chosen from the *ab initio* setup options menu.

For purposes of comparison, repeat the calculations using AM1 and PM3 semi-empirical calculations. Be sure to remove the restraint before obtaining the planar energy with a single point calculation just as you did above.

Method	Pyramidal Energy (kcal/mol)	Planar Energy (kcal/mol)	Difference	Bond Angle (Å)
ab initio				
AM1				
PM3				

Why would you expect the pyramidal form to be more stable than the planar form? Give a rational interpretation in terms of the kind of orbitals occupied by the lone pair.

The Pyramidal Nature of Aromatic Amines

Smith, Ulmer, and Gilbert did an extensive study of the pyramidal nature of the nitrogen center when an aromatic ring replaces one of the ammonia hydrogen, i.e. aniline and its derivatives. Here interaction between the lone pair (p) orbital on the nitrogen and the conjugated π system can stabilize the sp^2 conformation.

Their investigation centered on whether MNDO, AM1 or PM3 was better at describing the degree of bending of the –NH$_2$ out of the plane of the aromatic ring. Their conclusion was that AM1 was consistently better.

Carry their calculation one step further and compute some limits on the inversion barrier in aniline, i.e., how strongly non-planar are the bonds around nitrogen?

You will encounter a slightly different problem here than in the ammonia case. The HyperChem modelbuilder builds aniline as a flat molecule. Construct the flat aniline and carryout AM1 and PM3 calculations. The symmetry of the molecule will keep the aniline planar as it adjusts bond lengths with no restraints necessary.

Next, use the technique of turning off whole molecule translation (File-Preferences-Tools). Highlight the two amine hydrogen atoms and move them out of the plane. Repeat the geometry optimizations. Record the energy and the angles for each.

Method	Pyramidal Structure	Planar Structure	Energy Difference
AM1 Energy (kcal/mol)			
H-N-H angle			
C-N-H angle			
PM3 Energy (kcal/mol)			
H-N-H angle			
C-N-H angle			

Which form is more stable according to these calculations? Which result is closest to the experimental value? How does the inversion barrier for aniline compare with that of ammonia?

Reference

Smith, D. A.; Ulmer, C.W.; Gilbert, M. J. *J. Comp. Chem*, **1992**, 13, 640.

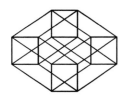

Chapter 5
Thermodynamics

"You see, therefore, that living force may be converted into heat, and that heat may be converted into living force, or its equivalent attraction through space. All three, therefore – namely, heat, living force, and attraction through space (to which I might also add light, were it consistent with the scope of the present lecture) – are mutually convertible into one another." - James Joule, 1847

Experiments conducted in the early 1840s by James Joule established that heat could be included in the conservation of energy principle that had been established for mechanical work, electrostatics and electrodynamics. It is intriguing to note that he added light as well!

This chapter includes exercises that make use of the heats of formation calculated by the various semi-empirical methods to account for the stability of chemical systems.

28. Heats of Formation of Conjugated Hydrocarbons

The reliability of computational methods can be tested using large sets of compounds to compare experimentally determined results with values obtained from various computational methods. Dewar *et al.* compared heats of formation, dipole moments and ionization energies of 58 hydrocarbons to compare MINDO/3, MNDO and AM1. In this exercise you will investigate a set of conjugated hydrocarbons and determine the average error in the heat of formation computed by two semi-empirical methods. Values of the standard gas phase enthalpies of formation are tabulated below. They can be used as benchmarks for evaluating the various semi-empirical methods.

Sketch each compound in the space provided. Draw and modelbuild each structure using HyperChem. Optimize the geometry using the specified semi-empirical method. The collection of data can be facilitated using the following script file. Create it as a text file and save it in the HyperChem Scripts directory (Hyper5/Scripts/ as heat-of-formation.scr.

```
; Script for Extracting Heat of Formation
; The structure is optimized using the
; semi-empirical method indicated.
;
calculation-method semi-empirical
semi-empirical-method am1
do-optimization
query-value heat-of-formation
```

Alternatively the heat of formation can be obtained from the log file. To avoid a very large file, it would be best to optimize the geometry first. Then open a log file in HyperChem and do a single point calculation. After closing the log file, it can be opened using a reader such as Notepad.

Experimental values are from the National Institute of Standards and Technology Web book, [http://webbook.nist.gov/chemistry/]. That site also gives the experimental error for each result. Be sure to specify gas phase thermodynamic data in kcal/mol if looking up the average experimental errors.

Mike Colvin of Lawrence Livermore Labs estimated the accuracy of calculations with the "most rigorous computational chemical methods" at ±1 kcal/mol, [http://guttenberg.llnl.gov/~colvin/]. Using the semi-empirical methods cited above, Dewar reported average errors ranging form 5-10 kcal/mole for the hydrocarbons he studied.

How do the average error for the semi-empirical PM3 and AM1 optimizations compare with the experimental gas phase values reported by NIST?

Use the NIST Web book to obtain the reported experimental errors. How do the average experimental errors compare with the average computed errors?

Reference

Dewar, M. J. S.; Zoebisch, E. G.; Healy, E. F.; Stewart, J. J. P. *J. Am. Chem. Soc.*, **1985**, 107, 3902-3909.

Compound	Structure	Δ_fH experimental (kcal/mol)	Δ_fH for PM3 optimized structure (kcal/mol)	Δ_fH for AM1 optimized structure (kcal/mol)
Ethylene		12.53		
trans-Butadiene		26.00, 26.75		
Benzene		19.82		
Naphthalene		35.99, 36.25		
Anthracene		55.17		
Phenanthrene		48.09, 49.46		
Pyrene		53.94		
Toluene		11.95		
o-Xylene		19.0		
m-Xylene		17.2		
p-Xylene		17.9		
1-Methyl-2-ethylbenzene		0.29		
1-Methyl-3-ethylbenzene		-0.46		
1-Methyl-4-ethylbenzene		-0.78		

29. The Heat of Combustion of Fuels

The move to use renewable fuel sources such as ethanol raises the question of just how much heat is stored gram for gram in the bonds of ethanol as compared to traditional hydrocarbon fuels. We will be examining the energy content of several fuels in this exercise.

Combustion is the process during which the carbon and hydrogen atoms of a fuel are oxidized, usually by atmospheric oxygen. For this exercise we will assume complete combustion occurs so the products are carbon dioxide and water. In an internal combustion engine, carbon monoxide or even carbon particles (soot) can form if a sufficient supply of air is not present.

Here you will explore several compounds used as fuels including an octane in both straight chain and branched structures. You will also look at how the calories per gram vary as a function of percent oxygen in the compound.

Draw each of the structures indicated on the table and optimize them using a semi-empirical method such as AM1. Extract the heat of formation from the log file or with a simple script file. You will also need the heat of formation for water and carbon dioxide.

After gathering the heat of formation data, write balanced chemical equations for the combustion of each fuel.

$$\text{Fuel} \;+\; O_2 \;\rightarrow\; CO_2 \;+\; H_2O$$

Use Hess's Law to calculate the molar heat of combustion of each fuel and calculate the kcal released per gram of fuel as well. Compare the amount of heat released per gram. How does it depend on the oxygen content?

What advantages does the use of ethanol have other than the fact this is a renewable resource? You may want to try an experiment such as the one described in the reference below to further explore this combustion process.

Reference

Laboratory Manual to Accompany Chemistry in Context 2nd ed.; WCB/McGraw-Hill: Dubuque, IA, 1997.

Compound	AM1 $\Delta_f H$ (kcal/mol)	% Oxygen	$\Delta_{comb} H$ (kcal/mol)	$\Delta_{comb} H$ (kcal/gram)
"Kerosene" $C_{11}H_{24}$				
"Octane" n-$C_8 H_{18}$				
"Iso-octane" 2,2,4-trimethylpentane				
Butanol $C_4 H_9 OH$				
Ethanol $C_2 H_5 OH$				
CO_2				
$H_2 O$				

30. Dehydration of 1-Butanol: the Stability of Alkenes

Dehydration of an alcohol such as 1-butanol produces a mixture of butenes: 1-butene, cis- and trans- 2-butene.

1-butene   cis-2-butene   trans-2-butene

The relative amounts of each of these products can be determined experimentally. By computing the energies of each isomer, we can estimate their relative stability. If the thermodynamic stability of the isomers is in agreement with the experimentally observed product distribution, the reaction is said to be under thermodynamic control. If not, it is said to be under kinetic control.

Modeling

Construct 1-butene, then modelbuild and do a geometry optimization. Record the energy for this structure. Repeat for cis- and trans- 2-butene.

Notice that 1-butene has two single C-C bonds. The HyperChem model builder and Geometry Optimizer do not necessarily optimize torsion angles (optimization finds the local minimum); in fact, the model builder occasionally assigns energetically unfavorable values. For this reason, it is a good idea to adjust some of the angles before concluding that a structure is stable.

View the molecule along the C-C single bonds and look for strained (eclipsed) conformers. To change the value of a torsional angle, select the four atoms defining the angle. From the Edit menu, choose Set Bond torsion and enter the desired value. For mouse-controlled rotations about a bond use the select tool. Double click on the rotation bond. This selects the bond and everything to one side of it. Using the z-rotate tool, R-drag to rotate about the bond. Re-optimize the geometry and save the structure of the most stable conformers of each isomer.

Both the MM+ energy and the heat of formation from a semi-empirical calculation can be used to determine the relative stability of isomers.

30. Dehydration of 1-Butanol: the Stability of Alkenes

The heat of formation can also be compared directly with the experimental values in the table.

Isomer	MM+ Energy (kcal/mol)	Δ_fH (calculated) (kcal/mol)	Δ_fH (experimental) (kcal/mol)
1-butene			0.02
cis-2-butene			-1.70
trans-2-butene			-2.72

From your results, predict which isomer should predominate in the product mixture. If you have carried out the experiment and performed a GC analysis of the product, comment on the extent of agreement between your predictions and the experimental results. Is this reaction under thermodynamic or kinetic control?

To automate optimization and report the heat of formation and dipole moment directly to the HyperChem workspace: Enter the following text using any text editor, and save it as c:\hyper\yourfile.scr. To run the script from HyperChem you choose Script/Open Script and select yourfile.scr.

```
; This is the script file associated with alkane
;stabilityexperiment.
;
;
; Geometry optimization of structure in active
; window, using current
; setup values and computational method.
; Detailed output will go to
; chem.log.
; Open log file "chem.log"
; "no" = do not append to previous file
;
start-logging chem.log no
do-optimization
append-omsgs-to-file chem.log
stop-logging
;
; Save resulting structure in chem.hin
;
write-file chem.hin
;
; Confirm convergence and values of heat of formation
; and dipole moment to screen. For molecular mechanics energy
; contributions, substitute ; total-energy, stretch-energy,
; bend-energy, torsion-energy, etc. ;omsgs-not-to-file
query-value optim-converged
query-value heat-of-formation
query-value dipole-moment
exit-script
```

31. Stability of Dibenzalacetone Isomers

In the synthesis of dibenzalacetone by aldol condensation of acetone with benzaldehyde1 the primary product melts at 110-112° C and has a intense uv absorption at 330 nm. Two other isomers are known.

Experimental data on the three isomers are summarized in the table below.

Isomer #	Melting point (°C)	UV spectrum λ (nm)	UV spectrum ε ($M^{-1}cm^{-1}$)
1	110-111	330	34,300
2	60	295	20,000
3	< 20	287	11,000

What are the structures of these three isomers? Does the most stable isomer predominate in the product mixture? We will use molecular mechanics and semi-empirical methods to evaluate the relative stabilities of the isomers of dibenzalacetone. We begin with the three geometric isomers, each of which has a number of stable conformations. Once these are identified, the energies may be evaluated by a batch method using Microsoft Excel.

By considering the relative stability of each isomer, the ease with which it would pack into a crystalline lattice, its dipole moment and the planarity of its conjugated electronic system you will be able to associate a structure with each of the isomers for which data are available.

Batch Calculations on Sets of Molecules

If you have access to Microsoft Excel and wish to automate operations in HyperChem, the good news is that you can! HyperChem comes equipped with this capability as well as a spreadsheet (PLOT.XLS) and a macro (PLOT.XLM) all set up to run MM+ Single Point Energy calculations on a set of molecular structure files that also come with HyperChem. Once you see how these pieces work, you can modify them to suit your own needs or create entirely new applications. Some facility in the use of multiple applications in Windows and with Microsoft Excel is needed.

Build the three geometric isomers of dibenzalacetone. Rotate about the single C-O bonds to generate conformational isomers of each of these. Save each unique structure and remember the names! Set up (but do not carry out) a molecular mechanics, MM+ calculation.

Start up Excel. Beginning at about line 5 of a new spreadsheet, enter the names of the dibenzaldehyde structure files in a column, omitting the ".HIN" extension. These names will be read in sequentially and the results of calculations will be recorded in the row next to each filename.

Now get the macro that runs the calculations and records the results. Under FILE choose OPEN and look in the \hyper\ directory for PLOT.XLM. Refer to the HyperChem manual, "Getting Started," for a line-by line guide to the commands in this macro.

To initiate the calculation, return to the spreadsheet window and place the cursor in the cell that contains the first structure file name. Click once to select this cell as the active cell. Then under the Excel Macro menu choose Run. In the dialog box pick PLOT.XLM!Compute.Results to run the macro.

Numbers will be recorded in the spreadsheet. What are they? Refer back to PLOT.XLM to find out. After the last "EXECUTE" command in the macro are a series of data transfer statements, each beginning with "FORMULA.ARRAY(REQUEST...). From these we see that the first column reports the total energy, followed by: stretch-energy, bend-energy, torsion-energy, nonbond-energy, and electrostatic energy. Enter column headings to identify these contributions to the MM+ total energy.

Compare the MM+ energies to identify the most stable conformer. It may be instructive to rank the conformers in order of decreasing stability, and to compare (perhaps overlay) structures whose energies are close.

Recall that this calculation did not perform a geometry optimization on any of the structures. To perform the same batch calculation with an energy minimization/geometry optimization, or to otherwise modify the calculation, read on!

Customizing the Calculation

The simplest change to make does not involve any modification of the macro at all. Recall that it was in HyperChem, under "Set Up" that the MM+ method was selected. To perform a semi-empirical calculation, simply go back to the SetUp menu and make another choice! Then proceed as before. If you are not doing an MM+ calculation, you may wish to delete the lines in PLOT.XLM that ask HyperChem for stretch, bend, etc. contributions to the energy.

Further Changes - Batch Calculations on Sets of Molecules

By making simple changes in the macro PLOT.XLM, you can tailor the calculations and the output to suit your needs. BE SURE TO SAVE PLOT.XLM "AS IS" BEFORE MAKING CHANGES. Save each modified macro under a different name.

Statement to be changed	Change to:
do-single-point	do-optimization
=FORMULA.ARRAY(REQUEST(Channel,"total-energy"),"rc[1]")	=FORMULA.ARRAY(REQUEST(Channel,"heat-of-formation"),"rc[1]")
None; add a line after total energy	=FORMULA.ARRAY(REQUEST(Channel,"dipole-moment"),"rc[2]")

Reference

Williamson, K.W.; Feiser, L. F. *Organic Experiments*, 7th ed.; Heath: New York, 1992.

32. Intermolecular Hydrogen Bonding

Jurema and Shields (1992) carried out an extensive, systematic examination of the ability of PM3 calculations to reproduce intermolecular hydrogen bonding. They found the method was satisfactory with a slight underestimation of bond lengths (0.1-0.2 Å) and energies (1-2 kcal/mol). In this lab, you will explore a number of hydrogen-bonded molecules to become familiar with the kinds of results one can expect.

The strength of the hydrogen bonds can be estimated by extracting the heats of formation for the geometry-optimized complex and subtracting the heat of formation of the individual geometry-optimized components.

$$\Delta_{association}H = \Delta_f H \text{ (complex)} - \Delta_f H(A) - \Delta_f H(B)$$

The paper contains a good explanation of why PM3 produces better hydrogen-bonding results than does AM1 (or MNDO).

Water-Formaldehyde

For comparison calculations with Jurema and Shields, experiment with the water-formaldehyde hydrogen bonded complexes. They report the formation of two different possible complexes, one in which the two water hydrogen are symmetrically connected to the formaldehyde oxygen, the other in which the bonding is a more familiar one with the water and formaldehyde oxygens and one hydrogen are in a straight line.

Draw and minimize each component separately. Determine the heat of formation of each molecule. Merge the two files by opening one and selecting Merge from the File menu to open the other.

Orienting the molecules can be tricky. Turn on Molecules in the selection menu. Select formaldehyde. Choose one of the rotation tools and R-drag until the molecule is oriented in the plane of the workspace. Sometimes it helps to display the inertial axes. (Display menu) Repeat with the water molecule, moving it to one of the orientations indicated. The OH_2 on the left approaches at an angle to the plane of the formaldehyde.

Carry out a geometry optimization calculation for both forms of complex, using PM3. Use Display and Recompute Hydrogen Bonds to show them. Calculate the strength of the hydrogen bonds by extracting the heats of formation for each geometry-optimized complex and subtracting the heats of formation of geometry-optimized water and formaldehyde.

Formic Acid Dimer

Carry out a formic acid dimer calculation by creating formic acid, minimizing the structure using PM3 and saving it. Obtain the heat of formation for the optimized monomer from the log file. With a copy still in the workspace, merge it with the saved copy. Rotate the molecules to line them up as shown. Do a PM3 geometry optimization (to 0.1 convergence). Calculate the strength of this hydrogen bond as shown above. Measure the distances in your structure and compare them to the ones shown that were obtained by an *ab initio* calculation.

If you can spare the time (a couple of days to a week depending on your computer), carry out an *ab initio* calculation at a level comparable to that in the reference in Jurema and Shields.

Water

Does water prefer a structure with a single hydrogen bond or a bifurcated structure similar to the structures drawn for formic acid? This can be explored at both semi-empirical (MNDO, AM1, PM3) and *ab initio* (STO-3G or 6-31G**) levels since it is a small system.

Trifluoroethanol, CF_3CH_2OH

Trifluoroethanol is used in polypeptide and protein folding studies. For unknown reasons, without this molecule, proteins do not fold spontaneously in aqueous solutions. Because of the strong hydrogen inductive effect of the fluorine, the oxygen has a lower than usual electron density. The result is that the two forms of hydrogen bonding possible for this compound with water have different strengths. Determine which of the two forms is stronger. Here, it is instructive to observe the relative charges on the H---O-H centers as well to support the heat of association results.

Base Pairs

Besides those in ice, the most famous hydrogen bonds are the ones that hold the base pairs of DNA together in the double helix. Extensive studies have been done of all the many possible combinations of bases (see Jeffrey and Saenger). As examples, look at the pairs that appear in DNA, the adenosine-thymine (A-T) and guanine-cytosine (G-C) pairs. Two pieces of information should be extracted from your calculation. The first is the association energy when the pairs form. The second is a structural feature that must contribute to the proper pairing of A-T and G-C informing the helix.

Thymine   Adenine

Cytosine   Guanine

If the two pairs are drawn as shown, with each base attached to a carbon representing the connection to the ribose backbone of the chain, the distance between the two carbons should be roughly 1Å.

In your calculations, you will construct the two bases and optimize each geometry independently. Then merge the files and rotate or move each molecule until the appropriate hydrogens are in the right place to provide the hydrogen bonds between the pair. A geometry optimization, which is a long, slow process, will eventually create the base pairing via hydrogen bonding using PM3.

References

Chang, Y. –T; Yamaguchi, Y.; Miller, W.H.; Schaefer, J. *J. Am. Chem. Soc.* **1987**, 109, 7245.

Hehre, W. J.; Radom, L.; Schleyer, P.V.R; Pople, J. A. *Ab Initio Molecular Orbital Theory*; Wiley; New York, **1986.**

Jeffrey, G.A.; Saenger, W. *Hydrogen Bonding in Biological Structures;* Springer-Verlag: Berlin, 1991.

Jurema, M.W.; Shields, G.C. *J. Comp. Chem.* **1993,** 14, 89.

Solomons, T. W. Graham *Organic Chemistry, 2nd ed.* Wiley: New York, 1980

33. Steric Energies of Cubanes

Recent synthetic advances in cubane chemistry have spurred research into applications of the box-shaped eight-carbon compound. Cubane itself is a strained compound. Nitrocubanes have been studied recently as potential explosives. You will compute and compare the standard enthalpies of formation and combustion of n-octane, cubane, two nitrocubanes, and trinitrotoluene (TNT) in this exercise. From this data you will evaluate their potential as fuels and explosives.

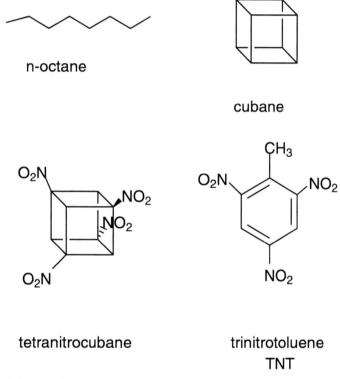

n-octane

cubane

tetranitrocubane

trinitrotoluene
TNT

Build each of the structures listed in the table. Optimize using molecular mechanics (MM+). Compute the standard heats of formation, $\Delta_f H^\circ$, using a PM3 semi-empirical method in a single point calculation. If you have time, optimize the structures using PM3. This takes longer.

Enter the data in the table below. Note also whether $\Delta_f H^\circ$ was determined from a single point calculation (faster and acceptable with an MM+ minimized structure) or a full geometry optimization (preferred). For the heat of combustion calculation, you will also need to compute $\Delta_f H°$ for CO_2 and H_2O using the same method. Then write the balanced equations for the reaction of each of the compounds with oxygen and determine the heat of combustion. Finally, compute the heat released per gram of compound and evaluate the suitability of each as a fuel and as an explosive.

Compound	MM+ Energy (kcal/mol)	PM3 $\Delta_f H$ (kcal/mol)	$\Delta_{comb}H$ (kcal/mol)	$\Delta_{comb}H$/gram (kcal/mol)
Octane				
Cubane				
Tetranitrocubane				
Octanitrocubane				
Trinitrotoluene				
Carbon Dioxide				
Water				

34. Tautomerism of 7-Aminopyrazolo pyrimidine

A series of C-nucleosides with a wide range of biological and pharmacological properties have the aromatic 7-aminoprazolo-pyrimidine structure in common. One, formacin, is similar to adenosine and can interact with physiological targets like adenosine kinase, adenosine deaminase (ADA). Its activity is related to an enzyme bound structure where the donor enzyme forms hydrogen bonds at N3 and N7. The presence of a hydrogen atom at N3 or N7 leads to enzyme inhibition.

7-aminopyrazolopyrimidine (N7H) can exist in tautomeric equilibrium with an N8H form as shown below. A comparison of the tautomeric preference of the protonated structure relative to the neutral state will be carried out in this exercise using semi-empirical methods.

N7H tautomer   N8H tautomer

Build the N7H isomer of neutral 7-aminopyrazolopyrimidine. Optimize the geometry with molecular mechanics, and then compute its enthalpy of formation using a single point AM1 calculation. Record the result. Save the structure. Repeat the calculation for the N8H isomer determining its heat of formation.

Next determine the relative stability of the protonated tautomers by adding a proton at either N1 or N3. Repeat the calculation. It will be necessary to select "Allow Ions" as you build the molecule. When doing the semi-empirical calculation use the options menu to set the charge to +1 and multiplicity to 1.

	ΔH Neutral Form (kcal/mol)	ΔH N1-Protonated Form (kcal/mol)	ΔH N3 Protonated Form (kcal/mol)
N7			
N8H			
Δ(ΔH) N7H-N8H			

There is experimental evidence that the N7H tautomeric form is most stable, however, leading to the hypothesis that the tautomeric preference changes from the N7H to the N8H tautomer upon binding. This hypothesis is supported at the 3-21G/3-21G level but not if electron correlation (MP4/6-31G*) is included.

Compare the enthalpy differences Δ(ΔH) defined as N7H-N8H with those obtained by Orozco and Luque shown below.

Method	*Ab initio* 3-21G/3-21G (kcal/mol)	*Ab initio* MP4/6-31G (kcal/mol)	This work (kcal/mol)
Neutral Form	-2.6	0.9	
N1-protonated	7.8	8.1	
N3-protonated	4.4	4.9	

Do your semi-empirical calculations support the hypothesis?

Reference

Orozco, M.; Luque, F. J. *J Am. Chem. Soc.* **1995**, 117, 1378-1386.

35. Resonance Energy: Benzene and Hexasilabenzene

The exceptional character of benzene among organic compounds has been known for many years. The unusual behavior has been attributed to "aromacity" based on its having $(4n + 2)\pi$ electrons according to the Hückel rule. The resonance stabilization of benzene can be determined experimentally with a bomb calorimeter by measuring the heats of combustion of benzene, cyclohexane and the cyclododecatriene shown below, using Hess's Law to construct a thermodynamic cycle. It may also be computed with considerably less effort from the enthalpy change for the following reaction.

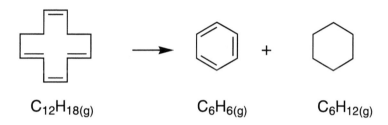

$$C_{12}H_{18(g)} \qquad\qquad C_6H_{6(g)} \qquad\qquad C_6H_{12(g)}$$

The reaction enthalpy is calculated from Hess's Law

$$\Delta_{rxn}H \quad = \quad \Delta_fH\ (C_6H_6) \quad + \quad \Delta_fH\ (C_6H_{12}) \quad - \quad \Delta_fH(C_{12}H_{18})$$

This heat of reaction is related to the resonance energy of benzene since (ΔU) the number of bonds of each type (C-C, C=C and C-H) is the same on both sides of the equation.

$$\Delta_{rxn}H \quad = \quad \Delta U \ + \ RT$$

Hexasilabenzene, the analog of benzene in which all carbons are replaced with silicon, also has $4n + 2$ electrons. The question of its structure and aromaticity has been the subject of study of several research groups. In this exercise you will use the same method to determine if hexasilabenzene shows the same degree of resonance stabilization as benzene.

Calculating Resonance Energy

Build each molecule. Optimize the geometry using AM1. Obtain the heat of formation from the log file or use a script file. Calculate the heat of reaction. Finally, compute ΔU as shown. The known (experimental) value for benzene is 36.0 kcal/mol.

Determine the resonance stabilization for hexasilabenzene in the same manner.

Compound	$\Delta_f H$ (kcal/mol)	Silicon Analog	$\Delta_f H$ (kcal/mol)
Benzene C_6H_6		Si_6H_6	
Cyclohexane C_6H_{12}		Si_6H_{12}	
Cyclododecatriene $C_{12}H_{18}$		$Si_{12}H_{18}$	
ΔU			

Hint: Remember to compute RT in kcal/mol!

Do your results indicate that hexasilabenzene is resonance stabilized?

Further Study

Sax, Kalcher and Janoschek investigated several isomers of hexasilabenzene. Build each of the following structures and optimize using AM1.   After extensive studies they concluded that isomer 2 below was the most stable. Do your results support this conclusion? Which is the most stable? Which is the least stable?

Isomer 1   Isomer 2

Isomer 3

Isomer 4

References

Clabo, D. A.; Schaefer, H.F. *J. Chem. Phys.* **1986**, 84, 1664-1669.

Nagase, S.; Teramae, H.; Kudo, T. *J. Chem. Phys.* **1987**, 86, 4513-4517.

Sax, A. F.; Kalcher, J.; Janoschek, R *J. Comp. Chem.* **1988**, 9, 564-577.

36. Flavin Redox Chemistry

Flavoenzymes are biological catalysts that offer a wide range of redox activity depending on substituents. Recently a study of the redox activity of flavin model compounds was reported in the literature. That study found a linear correlation with Hammett sigma (σ) values. Such linear free energy relationships are useful in interpreting mechanistic behavior of flavin-mediated reactions.

Reduction of the flavin model compounds requires that an electron is added to the molecule and this is most likely to occur at the lowest unoccupied molecular orbital, the LUMO. Here, we will see if the reported reduction potentials correlate with the energy of the LUMO.

Draw and model build each of the structures in the table. Optimize the geometry using AM1. Use the Compute menu selecting Orbitals to view the molecular orbital diagram and determine the energy of the LUMO. Prepare a graph of $E°$ versus LUMO energy to determine if a linear relationship exists.

From your knowledge of electron donor-acceptor properties, rationalize any trends related to substituent effects. The paper proposes that the substituent effect (withdrawing or releasing) relative to N5 is important in the mechanism. Thus they consider that C7 is meta and C8 is para to N5. Notice too that in these compounds substitution at C7 and C8 would not lead to steric hindrance at nitrogen 10 where the ribityl group would be connected in active forms. Substitution at C9 however could lead to steric hindrance. Isomer numbers are from the referenced article. Redox potentials for other substituents (F, Cl, and CN) are included in the article if you wish to extend this study..

Reference

Hasford, J. J.; Rizzo, C. J. *J. Am. Chem. Soc.* **1998**, 120, 2251-2255.

Isomer Number in reference	C_7	C_8	C_9	E° in mV at pH 7.4 vs. Ag/AgCl	AM1 LUMO (eV)
9	H	H	H	-407	
10	CH_3	H	H	-419	
11	H	CH_3	H	-439	
12	CH_3	CH_3	H	-456	
22	OCH_3	H	H	-396	
23	H	$N(CH_3)_3$	H	-580	
26	H	H	CH_3	-357	
27	CH_3	H	CH_3	-370	
28	H	CH_3	CH_3	-368	

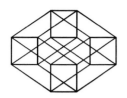

Chapter 6
Charge Distributions

"The more progress physical science makes, the more they tend to enter the domain of mathematics, which is a kind of centre to which they all converge. We may even judge the degree of perfection to which a science has arrived by the facility with which it may be submitted to calculation." - A. Quetelet, 1828

Unsymmetrical distribution of charge within a molecule gives rise to the experimental property called dipole moment. Polar molecules have permanent dipole moments. Non-polar molecules in the presence of external fields can acquire induced dipole moments.

The exercises in this chapter are all related to dipole moments. The first three focus on permanent dipole moments. Another is related to the transfer of charge as a molecule enters an excited state.

37. Permanent Dipole Moments

Experimentally, dipole moments of molecules such as HCl and C_6H_5Cl can be determined by measuring the macroscopic dielectric constant of a sample in dilute solution or in the gas phase. The ease of computation of molecular dipole moments makes it feasible to carry out computational "experiments" as well. Bond dipoles will be computed. The vector addition rule will be compared with direct calculations of dipole moments for molecules having two polar bonds.

The vector addition rule states that the dipole moment of a molecule is the vector sum of individual bond dipoles.

$$\mu^2 = \mu_1^2 + \mu_2^2 + 2\,\mu_1\mu_2\cos\theta$$

where θ is the angle between the individual bond dipole vectors. If $\mu_1 = \mu_2$ this simplifies to

$$\mu = 2\,\mu_1^2 + 2\,\mu_1\cos\left(\tfrac{1}{2}\,\theta\right)$$

Script to Gather Dipole Moments

Build each of the molecules shown in the table. Use the specified methods to optimize the geometry and determine the dipole moment. Use of the script file below will simplify data collection or open a log file to obtain the results.

```
;Script to calculate dipole moments
;using several methods:
;
calculation-method semi-empirical
semi-empirical-method pm3
do-optimization
query-value dipole-moment
;
semi-empirical-method cndo
do-optimization
query-value dipole-moment
;
semi-empirical-method AM1
do-optimization
query-value dipole-moment
```

Compute the root mean square deviation for each method.

	PM3	CNDO	AM1	Experiment (D)
HCl				1.08
Chlorobenzene				1.69
Acetonitrile				3.92
Dimethyl ether				1.30
RMS deviation for Method				

*Method root mean square deviation is $\sqrt{(\sum d_i^2 / n)}$

Using the bond dipole moment of monochlorobenzene from the best method as the C-Cl bond moment, compute the dipole moments for the compounds listed below by the vector addition method. Compare these values with the results of the quantum calculation.

	Angle (°)	Vector Addition Method	Quantum Mechanical Calculation	Experiment (D)
o-Dichlorobenzene				2.50
m-Dichlorobenzene				1.72
Chloromethane				1.87
Dichloromethane				1.60

The three compounds in the table below comprise a striking example of the failure of the simple picture we've been using so far. We expect that all will have approximately the same dipole moment due to two polar C-O bonds. They don't. What physical phenomena are we ignoring? Does a quantum calculation reproduce the observed trend? Complete the vector addition calculations. How might contour plots of electronic properties be useful in interpreting your results? Hint: you must consider polarization of adjacent bonds in order to rationalize these results.

Molecule	Vector Addition Method	PM3 Calculation	Experiment (D)
Dimethyl ether			1.30
Diethyl ether	(same as above)		1.20
Tetrahydrofuran	(nearly same as above)		1.60

References

McClellan, A. L. *Tables of Experimental Dipole Moments*, Freeman: San Francisco, 1963.

Shoemaker, D. P..; Garland, C. W.; Nibler, J. W. *Experiments in Physical Chemistry, 5th ed.*; McGraw-Hill: New York, 1988; pp 390-402.

38. Dipole Moment of Flexible Molecules

Succinonitrile is a conformationally flexible polar molecule. As a 1,2-disubstituted ethane it is one of the simplest to study theoretically. Experimental determination of the dielectric constant of succinonitrile in dilute solution is straight forward and leads to an experimental value for the mean square dipole moment $<\mu^2>$. This average depends on the distribution of molecules among three rotational states: trans, gauche+ and gauche-. The C-C-C-C torsion angle for trans is 180°; gauche conformations are at ±120°. The value for ΔE is the trans-gauche energy difference. Experimental details are given in the reference cited below.

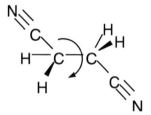

The computational experiment consists of calculation of ΔE for the isolated molecule with the expectation that the effect of the non-polar solvent medium is small.

Determine the bond moment for C-C≡N by constructing acetonitrile, $CH_3C \equiv N$. Optimize the geometry using a semi-empirical calculation to determine its dipole moment. Use this bond dipole (μ_1^2) in the calculation below.

To calculate the average dipole moment, $<\mu^2>$, build and optimize the trans and gauche rotational isomers of succinonitrile. It can be shown using appropriate Boltzmann population analysis that the trans-gauche energy difference, ΔE, is related to the mole fraction of the trans isomer as follows. Remember that HyperChem gives energies in kcal/mol. Use an appropriate value for R.

$$X_{trans} \quad = \quad (1 + 2 \exp(-\Delta E/RT))^{-1}$$

From X_{trans} the mean-square dipole moment can be calculated from the relation

$$<\mu^2> \quad = \quad (8/3)(1 - X_{trans})\,(\mu_1^2)$$

Compare your results to the experimental values.

Experimental Data

	PM3 Energy (kcal/mol)	PM3 Dipole Moment (D)
$CH_3C{\equiv}N$		
Gauche-succinonitrile		
Trans-succinonitrile		

Calculated Results

	Experiment	Calculated
$\Delta E = E(gauche) - E(trans)$		
X_{trans}		
$<\mu^2>$		
$< \mu >$		

References

Shoemaker, D. P.; Garland, C. W.; Nibler, J.W. *Experiments in Physical Chemistry, 5th ed.*; McGraw-Hill: New York, 1988, pp 390-402

Braun, C. L.; Stockmayer, W. H.; Orwall, R. A. *J. Chem. Ed.* **1970**, 47, 287.

39. The Effect of Dielectric Medium on Rotational States

While no molecular solvent behaves as a continuous dielectric medium on a microscopic scale, it is interesting to study the effect of such a medium on the relative populations of trans and gauche- rotational states of succinonitrile. Specifically, we would like to know how the populations change in a "polar" medium. To mimic this, you can use an MM+ calculation with the atomic charge option. Changing the scale factor has the effect of changing the dielectric constant.

In the preceding calculations you used a semi-empirical method to evaluate dipole moments. Molecular mechanics (MM+) offers that option as well. There are two ways to do this. The method is chosen with settings in the Options box. The simplest way uses bond dipole values that are specified in the MM+ stretch parameter file.

In this exercise you will use the other method that involves setting atomic charges. The charges must be estimated using a semi-empirical method. The advantage of this is that you can vary a scaling factor to mimic the effect that the medium would have on the system.

You will contrast the data obtained using each method as well as looking at the effect of the dielectric medium on the fraction of isomers in each form.

Bond Dipole Method

Build and save the gauche and trans forms of succinonitrile if you do not have them from the previous experiment. Optimize the geometry using MM+ with the bond dipole option selected. This is the default setting. Obtain the dipole moment and energy for each using MM+. Record the values in the table.

Atomic Charges

Use one of the semi-empirical methods such as AM1 or PM3 to get the charges. Do a single point calculation on each structure and save the file again. This will save the charges. You can use Display-Label if you want to see the charges on each atom.

Reset the calculation for molecular mechanics MM+. On the Options menu select Atomic Charges. Do an optimization to get the energy and extract the dipole moment from the log file or using a script file.

Changing the Dielectric Medium

The charges enter the energy expression via a term in the form of $q_1q_2/\varepsilon r_{12}$ where ε is the dielectric constant. A fourfold increase in ε is equivalent to reducing each atomic charge to half its initial value.

Do this by using the select tool (atoms) and Set Charge on the Build menu. Change the charge on each of the ten atoms to one-half of the value indicated. You can change the charge on more than one atom at the same time if they have the same initial value.

Re-optimize and extract the energy and dipole moment for both the trans and gauche forms.

Calculate the fraction of molecules in the trans form and the average dipole moment as you did in the previous exercise.

	Bond Dipole Method		Atomic Charge Method $\varepsilon = 1$		Atomic Charge Method $\varepsilon = 4$	
	μ (D)	Energy (kcal/mol)	μ (D)	Energy (kcal/mol)	μ (D)	Energy (kcal/mol)
Trans						
Gauche						

40. Charge Transfer and Excited State Dipole Moments

The nonlinear optical properties of certain conjugated organic molecules with electron donating and accepting groups have led to their use in data storage, telecommunications, and information processing applications. They also exhibit very interesting chemical behavior due to the redistribution of charge upon excitation. This phenomenon gives rise to intense electronic spectral bands that are strongly solvent dependent (Solvatochromic) and electric-field dependent (Electrochromic)

The behavior of these bands in substituted benzene compounds has been well studied experimentally; they are also accessible by computational methods. You will study the effect of donor and acceptor strength on the electronic spectra and related properties for several substituted benzene compounds in this exercise. Changes in charge distribution by variations in position using the same substituents will also be explored. The molecular properties of interest are the energy (wavelength) and intensity of the transition (oscillator strength) and the change in dipole moment upon excitation.

Identification of Charge Transfer States

In the first part you will study the computed electronic spectra of aniline in order to identify the charge-transfer bands. Aniline contains the electron-donating group, $-NH_2$. Experimentally, charge-transfer bands are characterized by large extinction coefficients and by sensitivity of the transition to solvent polarity. These extinction coefficients are related to the change in dipole moment accompanying excitation, as electron density migrates from donor to acceptor. The solvent dependence of the transition is largely due to the solvent stabilization of the ground state.

You will compute and tabulate data on transition energy, oscillator strength and dipole moment changes ($\Delta\mu = \mu_{excited} - \mu_{ground}$) for several substituted benzene compounds. Three donors ($-NH_2$, $-OCH_3$, and $-C\equiv CH$) will be compared as the position of a common acceptor ($-NO_2$) is varied.

Build and optimize each compound shown on the table. Use either MM+ or one of the semi-empirical methods, AM1 or PM3. Save the structures.

Start a log file. Setup and run a ZINDO/S single point calculation with Configurations Interaction. Use the Singly Excited method and set the Orbital Criterion to 2 or 3 for both HOMO and LUMO. (The results shown were obtained using 3). When the calculation is complete, display the spectra and find the most intense peaks. Note the transition number.

Open the log file and extract the wavelength, oscillator strength and State Dipole moments for the most intense transitions. A portion of the aniline log files is given below as an example. The regions of interest are shown in bold.

```
ANILINE *****************************************************
      0 (Reference)  Absolute Energy      -1283.17883

           1     Spin S                  0.00
             State Dipole            1.3649
             State Dipole Components     0.0000   1.3649   0.0000


      6 (Transition) Excitation Energy        229.0 nm
                                  43677.1 1/cm
        1 ->    7  Spin S              -0.00
             State Dipole            4.4511
             Oscillator Strength     0.2654
             State Dipole Components     0.0000   4.4511   0.0000
             Transition Dipole Components  0.0000   3.5948  -0.0000


             Spin Up :  Occ. MO  -->  Unocc. MO  Coefficients
             ------------------------------------------------
                       18  -->    20           -0.667158


             Spin Down:  Occ. MO  -->  Unocc. MO  Coefficients
             ------------------------------------------------
                       18  -->    20            0.667158
      9 (Transition) Excitation Energy        190.1 nm
                                  52615.0 1/cm
        1 ->   10  Spin S              -0.00
             State Dipole            3.0368
             Oscillator Strength     0.8551
             State Dipole Components     0.0000   3.0368   0.0000
             Transition Dipole Components -5.8789  -0.0000   0.0000
```

```
Spin Up :  Occ. MO  -->  Unocc. MO  Coefficients
------------------------------------------------
         18  -->    19              0.381617
         17  -->    20             -0.586651

Spin Down:  Occ. MO  -->  Unocc. MO  Coefficients
------------------------------------------------
         18  -->    19             -0.381617
         17  -->    20              0.586651
```

```
11 (Transition) Excitation Energy          187.5 nm
                                        53334.7 1/cm
   1 ->  12  Spin S                    -0.00
        State Dipole            2.2582
        Oscillator Strength     0.9617
        State Dipole Components        0.0000    2.2582    0.0000
        Transition Dipole Components  -0.0000    6.1923   -0.0000

    Spin Up :  Occ. MO  -->  Unocc. MO  Coefficients
    ------------------------------------------------
             17  -->    19              -0.666294

    Spin Down:  Occ. MO  -->  Unocc. MO  Coefficients
    ------------------------------------------------
             17  -->    19               0.666294
```

From the tabulated data, identify the charge-transfer band and associated states for each compound.

Confirm your identification by viewing the electron densities for the ground state and the excited state associated with the CT transition. Adjust the view of the molecule so that you don't plot the nodal plan of the orbital.

Compare trends in donor strength of -NH_2, -OCH_3, and -$C\equiv CH$ in the reference states (μ_{gr}) and in the excited states (μ_{ex}). Are excited state substituent effects the same as ground state substituent effects? Discuss how reactivity in the excited state could be changed.

References

Sinha, H. K.; Yates, K. *J. Am. Chem. Soc.* **1991**, 113, 6062-6067.

Marder, S. R.; Beratan, N. N.; Cheng, L. –T. *Science*, **1991,** 252, 103.

Molecule and μ_{ground}	Transition Occup MO $\rightarrow$ Unocc.MO	λ (nm)	Oscillator Strength	$\mu_{excited}$	$\Delta\mu = \mu_{ex} - \mu_{gr}$
Aniline					
$\mu_{ground} = 1.3649$	$18 \rightarrow 19$	190.1	0.8551	3.0368	
	$17 \rightarrow 19$	187.5	0.9617	2.2582	
p-Nitroaniline					
$\mu_{ground} =$					
m-Nitroaniline					
$\mu_{ground} =$					
p-Nitromethoxy benzene					
$\mu_{ground} =$					
m-Nitromethoxy benzene					
$\mu_{ground} =$					

m-Nitrophenyl acetylene					
μ_{ground} =					

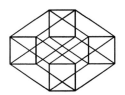

Chapter 7
Spectroscopy

"For the rest of my life, I want to reflect on what light is."

- Albert Einstein

The interaction of light with matter has captivated people for centuries. From the works of artists who mix pigments to chemists who create new pigments, the human spirit is enriched by the play of light on materials. Not only is our aesthetic life so enriched; as scientists began to use light to probe substances, a wealth of new information about atomic and molecular structure enriched our understanding of the nature of matter.

The electromagnetic spectrum provides us with an experimental tool to investigate the identity, structure and energy states of chemical systems. Several exercises are included here to demonstrate how computer modeling of spectroscopic transitions is now opening another avenue of investigation.

41. UV Spectra of Polycyclic Aromatic Hydrocarbons

Polycyclic aromatic hydrocarbons provide an opportunity for a study of the correlation between theory and experiment in UV-visible spectroscopy. The higher homologues of benzene follow the Hückel rule with 4n+2 π electrons. The long wavelength absorptions correspond to $\pi \rightarrow \pi^*$ transitions since the π orbitals are the highest occupied orbitals and the π^* antibonding orbitals are the lowest empty orbitals. Having said that, it turns out that matching computed results and a UV-visible spectrum involves more than looking up two numbers. We have to do some rummaging among the numbers to determine exactly which numbers might match up with which.

The Experimental Data

Molecule		β	p	α	τ
Naphthalene		221	289	315	470
Anthracene		255	379	---	670
Tetracene		274	471	---	976
Pentacene		310	576	428	1300
Phenanthrene		255	295	345	463

On the experimental side, the spectra of polycyclic aromatics contain several peaks labeled β (ε about 10^5), p (ε about 10^4), α (forbidden, ε about 10^2), and τ (spin forbidden, very weak). It is thought that the first three are singlet-singlet transitions and that p corresponds to $\psi_{HOMO} \rightarrow \psi_{LUMO}$, while β and α are some combination of the degenerate transitions $\psi_{HOMO-1} \rightarrow \psi_{LUMO}$, $\psi_{HOMO} \rightarrow \psi_{LUMO+1}$, with the α transition forbidden.

The Theoretical Mode

At the simplest level, the π electron orbitals may be modeled by a particle in a box. Energy level differences between levels are proportional to n, the level from which the electron is excited, and inversely proportional to L^2, the length of the box. Consequently, the π - π* gap should decrease in traversing the series naphthalene to pentacene as it does.

A rigorous theory of electronic spectra should take into account electron-electron interactions in both the ground and excited states and use the energy differences between states, not orbitals, as the measure of the transition energy. The procedure is to carry out a molecular orbital calculation of the ground state and create a set of excited states created by moving single electrons from filled orbitals to empty (virtual) orbitals. The various orbital configurations are used as a basis set for a further, less approximate solution to the molecular Schrödinger equation, resulting in an improved ground state energy as well as energies of low lying excited states.

------	------	----β-	------	-α---	------	----β-
------	----β-	------	-α---	------	----β-	------
-α-β-	-α---	-α---	-α---	-α---	-α-β-	-α-β-
-α-β-	-α-β-	-α-β-	-α-β-	-α-β-	-α---	-α---
-α-β-	-α-β-	-α-β-	-α-β-	-α-β-	-α-β-	-α-β-

etc.

Computing a Spectrum

HyperChem will produce an electronic spectrum for us rapidly and easily. To interpret the results, however, requires an examination of the numbers that accompany the graphical output. First, try producing a spectrum. Use naphthalene as the example and follow this procedure:

Given the size of the molecules in this study, a semi-empirical molecular orbital calculation is the reasonable choice. HyperChem offers eight methods that can be used with configuration interaction (CI) calculations. ZINDO/S was specifically parameterized by Zerner to give good agreement with spectral results but in this particular study, PM3 produces very good results, so we'll base our instructions on that method.

Before carrying out a CI calculation, build the molecule of interest and decide if you'll use the standard model built geometry or optimize the geometry. Geometry optimization could be done using a semi-empirical method such as PM3 or a molecular mechanics model such as MM+. Don't use ZINDO/S. Geometry is not its strong point.

To do a CI calculation requires three menu selections. First, use the Setup menu and choose the semi-empirical method desired. Then click on Options. Set the SCF Controls as shown below and be sure to check accelerate convergence. Finally, click on Configuration Interaction.

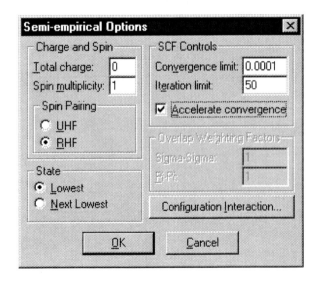

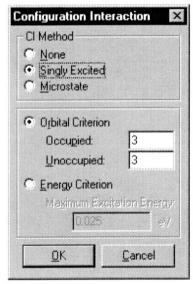

When the CI screen appears, choose Singly Excited. Look at the choice between orbital criterion and energy criterion. This is asking us if we want to use excited orbitals within a certain energy distance or whether we want to use some fixed number of occupied and unoccupied orbitals. The default choice of orbital criterion with the 3 topmost occupied orbitals and the 3 lowest unoccupied orbitals is not a bad starting point. When the calculation starts, you will see a message that 19 configurations are being used in the calculation. Determine that that is a correct statement. At some later time, try a larger CI calculation on naphthalene to see what the effect is. Once the options have been chosen, close each menu with its OK button.

Pull down the Compute menu and choose Single Point. Notice that the choices are limited. CI isn't used for geometry calculations or molecular dynamics here.

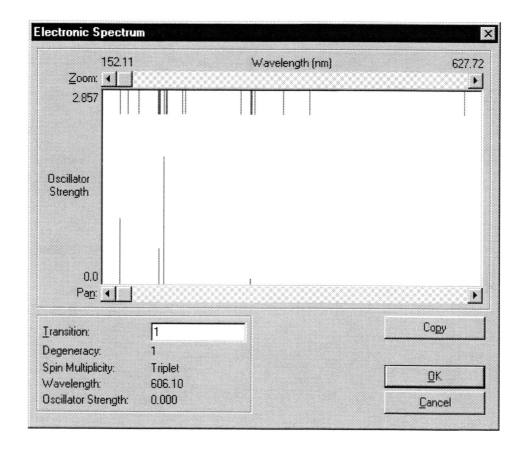

Once the CI calculation is completed, you can pull down the Compute menu again and have the Electronic Spectrum produced. Now the interpretation needs to begin. The spectrum consists of an upper set of lines indicating every computed transition resulting from the CI calculation, i.e., the energy from the ground state to each excited state. The lower set of lines is the spectrum of transitions again but with the line height representing the oscillator strength (intensity) of the transition. Many of the upper transitions are singlet-triplet transitions, thus spin forbidden. Starting at the longest wavelength line in the upper spectrum, click on each line and note whether the transition is to a triplet or singlet excited state. Fill in the column of Table 1 listing the excited state spin.

Once you've found the first 6 singlet states, stop. Let's now go and find out what orbitals those singlet transitions correspond to by using the HyperChem log file.

Log files

Behind the scenes of most calculations, HyperChem produces large quantities of numbers. Some appear on the status line at the bottom of the workspace but many more are lost. To gather this information, pull down the File menu at any time and choose Start Log. Choose a file name or use the default chem.log when asked. When you've recorded the information of interest, pull down File and Stop log.

The log file is a simple ASCII text file which any word processor, e.g., Notepad, can read. For this lab, we want to record information about the CI calculation on naphthalene, so you should now repeat the Single Point calculation for naphthalene just after turning on the log file. When it is complete, turn off the log file.

If you now open up the log file, you will find a list of the molecular orbitals from the PM3 computation. A fragment of that table appear here (hint - convert the file to a non-proportional font such as Courier).

```
Mol. Orbital      19        20        21        22        23        24
Eigenvalue    -12.39620 -12.26975 -11.86145 -10.69747 -9.51358  8.58734

  S   C   1   -0.01773  -0.00561   0.00000   0.00000   0.00000   0.0000
  Px  C   1    0.12385   0.20926   0.00000   0.00000   0.00000   0.00000
  Py  C   1    0.24377  -0.12288   0.00000   0.00000   0.00000   0.00000
  Pz  C   1    0.00000   0.00000   0.42317  -0.19022  -0.39250   0.26669
  S   C   2    0.01773  -0.00561   0.00000   0.00000   0.00000   0.00000
  Px  C   2   -0.14919  -0.21105   0.00000   0.00000   0.00000   0.00000
  Py  C   2   -0.22914   0.11979   0.00000   0.00000   0.00000   0.00000
```

The orbitals are laid out in columns with each column having the orbital energy at the top and the coefficients of the atomic orbitals down the column. Since HyperChem builds planar aromatic molecules in the xy plane, any orbital containing p_z atomic orbitals from a ring carbon it must be a pi orbital, e.g., orbitals 21 and 22 above. Search through the molecular orbitals in the file to find all of the pi orbitals and fill in the table below.

Number of valence atomic orbitals for $C_{10}H_8$	
Number of valence electrons for $C_{10}H_8$	
Highest Occupied Molecular Orbital:	
Orbital numbers for occupied pi orbitals:	
Orbitals numbers for unoccupied pi orbitals:	

If you move back up in the log file, you will find details about each electronic transition computed in the CI calculation. The transitions are numbered from the longest wavelength and so have the numbering from our transition table above.

Search through the transitions to find those which are the first six singlet-singlet transitions you had noted in Table 1. Take a look in some detail at the information about the transition. As an example, look at transition #6:

```
6 (Transition) Excitation Energy          338.0 nm
                                             29587.1 1/cm

1 -> 7  Spin S                0.00
           State Dipole              0.0000
           Oscillator Strength       0.1176

           State Dipole Components        0.0000    0.0000   0.0000
           Transition Dipole Components   2.5180   -1.4538   0.0000

Spin Up :  Occ. MO   -->  Unocc. MO  Coefficients
           ------------------------------------------------
                    24   -->    25              0.619441
                    23   -->    26             -0.335232

    Spin Down:  Occ. MO   -->  Unocc. MO  Coefficients
           ------------------------------------------------
                    24   -->    25             -0.619441
                    23   -->    26              0.335232
```

This is a singlet-singlet transition with some significant oscillator strength. It involves a mix of orbital changes but is primarily the transition $\psi_{HOMO} \rightarrow \psi_{LUMO}$. Complete the transtion table (Table 2) for the other singlet-singlet transitions and you can convince yourself that the assignments are probably:

- transition 4 is α, the long wavelength forbidden transition

- transition 6 is p, the allowed HOMO to LUMO transition

- transition 12 is β, the intense allowed transition

Proceed now through the rest of the polycyclic aromatics assigning the computed peaks to β, p, α.

Table 1

Transition #	Spin of excited state	Wavelength, λ (nm)	Oscillator strength	MOs Involved
1				
2				
3				
4				
5				
6				
7				
8				
9				
10				
11				
12				
13				
14				
15				
16				
17				
18				

Table 2

Molecule	β (intense peak) $\varepsilon \cong 1\text{-}2$	p (weaker, non-zero peak) $\varepsilon \cong 0.1$	α (forbidden, zero intensity) $\varepsilon = 0$
Naphthalene			
Anthracene			
Tetracene			
Pentacene			
Phenanthrene			

Reference

Rao, C. N. R. *Ultra-Violet and Visible Spectroscopy, 3rd ed.*, Butterworth: London, 1975.

42. Vibrational Spectra

An infrared spectrum of a molecule arises from the absorption of radiation that excites the vibrations in a molecule. In organic chemistry there will be jumbles of peaks corresponding to C-C and C-H stretches and bends and then often quite distinctive peaks showing functional groups. In this exercise, we'll examine double bond stretches in some small ring systems. In the first set of compounds the double bond is a C=C bond in the ring: in the second set, a C=O bond protruding from the ring. In the first series we will include acetylene as a model for a fictitious two carbon cyclic "alkene."

A theoretical infrared spectrum is computed by optimizing the geometry of a molecule using a semi-empirical molecular orbital calculation method. The optimization ensures that there are no forces acting on the atoms. Then the second derivatives of the energy are computed for the movement of each atom in the x, y, and z directions. The force matrix is diagonalized to solve for the energies and modes of vibration. The choice of MO method is based on experience. INDO, for example, seems to give outrageously high values for stretches, AM1 and PM3 give high but reasonable results. In this exercise, we suggest PM3, but feel free to experiment.

Computing the Infrared Spectrum

Construct the molecule and use the modelbuilder to obtain a starting geometry. Choose Semi-empirical methods and PM3 from the Setup menu and Geometry Optimization from the Compute menu.

Once the optimized geometry is obtained, choose Vibrations from the Compute menu. This part of the calculation is the most time-consuming (for the computer, not you.)

Before displaying the vibrational spectrum and a particular vibrational mode, go to the rendering menu (Display-Rendering) and select Sticks if that is not already chosen. Then click on the Sticks properties tab and check Wedges and IR vectors.

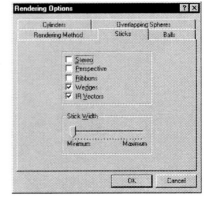

Choose vibrational spectrum from the Compute menu.

When you do, a spectrum will appear immediately. At the top will be a line for each normal mode in the molecule. At the bottom will be lines corresponding to the infrared active modes. The height of these represents the intensity of the vibration and is proportional to the change in dipole moment during the vibration. The spectrum for cyclohexene is shown below.

Fortunately, the double bond stretches we are studying stand out from the general background. They will appear near the center of the spectrum. The arrow points to the mode corresponding to the C=C stretch on the top section.

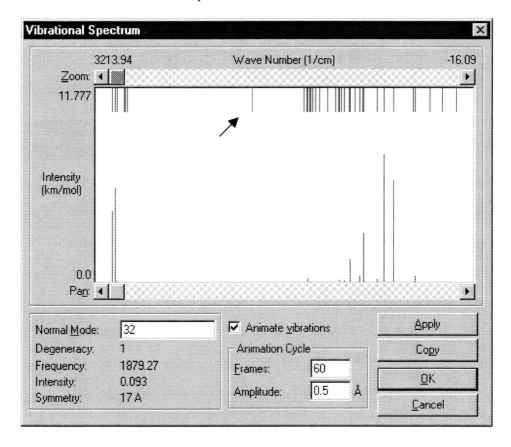

When you have chosen the peak, L-click the Animate Vibrations box, and then click OK. What you will see is a moving version of the molecule with vectors drawn indicating the direction of motion. If you have selected the correct vibration, the image should appear like the one at the right. Note that the long vectors shown the C=C is in motion.

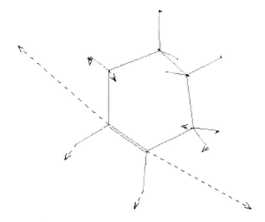

Record the frequency and the intensity of the vibration in the table provided.

The object of the exercise is to compute the energies of the C=C and C=O stretches. After you've collected those values, answer the following questions.

Discuss the fact that the C=C stretches are very low in intensity, zero in some cases, while the C=O stretches are quite intense.

What is behind the simple increase in the energy of the C=O vibrations as one goes down the series, i.e. as the ring gets smaller?

What factors are behind the decreasing, then increasing, energies of the C=C stretches in the cyclic alkenes?

Reference

Colthrup, N. B.; Daly, L. H.; Wiberley, S. E. *Introduction to Infrared and Raman Spectroscopy, 3rd ed.* Academic Press: San Diego, 1990.

Molecule	PM3 Frequency (cm^{-1})	PM3 intensity	Experimental Frequency (cm^{-1})
Alkenes C=C stretch			
Cyclohexene			1646
Cyclopentene			1611
Cyclobutene			1566
Cyclopropene			1641
Acetylene			1974
Cyclic ketones C=O stretch			
Cyclohexanone			1715
Cyclopentanone			1740
Cyclobutanone			1782
Cyclopropanone			1822

43. The Spectra of Visual Pigments

The accepted model photon interaction with rods and cones in the eye is that a photosensitive molecule called retinal exists in the rod or cone in its 11-cis form. The molecule is bound to a protein called opsin (MW ~38,000) by a Schiff's base linkage to an ε-amino group of a lysine side chain. The molecule absorbs light easily in the visible region (at about 500 nm) and uses the energy to convert 11-cis retinal to the all-trans-isomer. The all-trans-isomer no longer fits the binding site for the 11-cis isomer and hydrolysis of the Schiff's base linkage occurs. The 11-cis isomer is later regenerated by the action of enzymes.

This exercise will allow you to examine retinal and some other molecules closely associated with vision to see how the absorption peak changes as the structure changes.

All trans and 11-cis retinal

Consider first the two important forms of retinal. All-trans retinal does not absorb visible light but absorbs in the UV region at about 387 nm. For the first calculation, construct all trans-retinal as shown below. Note that carbon 11 is marked.

Using PM3 or AM1, optimize the structure to a convergence criterion

all-trans-retinal

of about 0.2 and the Steepest Descent convergence algorithm. Save the optimized structure. Finally, perform a single-point CI calculation by selecting Options on the setup menu and R-clicking the Configuration Interaction button. Check single excited method and set the orbital criterion to at least 2 for both the HOMO and LUMO. In general as you include more orbitals the calculation will take longer but the spectrum will be more accurate. Record your results in the table on the next page.

Use the edit function to convert the all trans to 11-cis retinal. Re-optimize the geometry and finally obtain the spectrum performing a single point CI calculation.

On the basis of Hückel theory, what change in wavelength would you expect for the absorption of light by 11-cis compared to all-trans-retinal?

Rhodopsins

A change in the absorption maximum for the 11-cis retinal arises from the complexation with the protein in the retina. The attachment is via a Schiff base.

$$R(C=O)H \quad + \quad H_2N\text{-protein} \quad \rightarrow \quad R\text{-}C=N^+H\text{-protein}$$

Calculations with a protein attached would be unreasonably long to say the least. Instead, try a simple model of the rhodopsin including the Schiff's base portion with a positive charge on the resulting molecule but representing the rest of the protein by a methyl group. Form both the trans and cis versions, optimize the geometry and do the CI calculations once more. Remember to set the charge. Record the wavelength and oscillator strength of the main peak.

Molecule	λ_{max} (nm) PM3	Oscillator Strength	λ_{max} (nm) Experimental	Extinction Coefficient ε $(M^{-1}cm^{-1})$
all-trans retinal				
11-cis retinal				
trans rhodopsin model			380	
11-cis rhodopsin model			500	40,000
all-trans vitamin A				
11-cis vitamin A				

Vitamin A

The precursor of 11-cis-retinal is all-trans-retinol (Vitamin A) in which the aldehyde is reduced to alcohol. Vitamin A appears even more bleached than the retinal, i.e. less able to absorb visible light. Carry out optimizations and CI calculations on the vitamin A molecules to complete the table above and see if you can back up that observation.

Further work

In these very simple model calculations, we have actually ignored the most interesting research question about the spectra of the visual pigments. Why does the absorption maxima vary from species to species from about 430 to 580 nm? The match between model rhodopsin and the absorption spectrum of rhodopsin in a typical animal visual pigment is somewhat fortuitous, as the simple protonated Schiff base of 11-cis retinal actually absorbs at about 440 nm. We need to examine how nature can tune the absorption to longer wavelengths.

Various models have been proposed. We will explore one called the point-charge perturbation model. It has been suggested that a negative point charge on a neighboring protein (e.g. a carboxylate anion) could alter the charge distribution in the rhodopsin by electrostatic interaction. Some have proposed it occurs near the Schiff base end while others have proposed an interaction close to the ring.

Build a formic acid anion and optimize it using the same method used to optimize the retinal structures. Save it. Open the 11-cis-retinal Schiff base file and merge it with the anion you just saved. Position the anion so one of its oxygen atoms is about 10Å from the nitrogen. This can be done easily by drawing a bond between the two and using Edit-Set bond length. Then remove the bond.

The system now has a zero charge and multiplicity of 1. Set up a CI calculation as before and do a single point calculation. Look at the spectrum. What effect did the point-charge have on the chromophore?

Move the carboxylate to a position about 10Å from the double bond in the ring? Again, compute the spectrum and record the absorption maxima.

Try other positions or distances from the indicated positions.

Point Charge Position relative to 11-cis-retinal Schiff Base	λ_{max} (nm)
11-cis rhodopsin model from above	
11-cis rhodopsin model	
One about 10 Å from N^+	
One about 10 Å from ring C=C	

Discuss the shifts in terms of the Hückel theory.

References

Stryer, Lubert *Biochemistry;* Freeman; San Francisco, 1975.

Balogh-Nair, V. ; Nakanishi, K*;* In *Stereochemistry*; Tamm, Ed.; Elsevier: Amsterdam, 1982, Chapter 7.

44. Solvent Effects on Spectra

Absorption of light in the visible region (700 to 400 nm) and the near ultraviolet region (400 to 200 nm) of the electromagnetic spectrum results in electronic transitions for both organic and inorganic compounds.

Absorption of light by the electrons of a single sigma (σ) bond occurs in the vacuum-ultraviolet region (below 180 nm) where atmospheric components also absorb strongly. Obtaining spectra for these transitions is experimentally difficult but can be computed using HyperChem. In general, experimental spectra are limited to absorption by various functional groups, or chromophores, which contain lower energy valence electrons. Chromophores usually contain either unshared electrons which are localized on atoms such as oxygen, sulfur, nitrogen, or halogens (nonbonding electrons) or bonding electrons such as those found in double and triple bonds. The commonly encountered transitions are: $n \rightarrow \sigma^*$, $n \rightarrow \pi^*$, and $\pi \rightarrow \pi^*$.

Such transitions can be distinguished by their molar absorptivity. For $n \rightarrow \pi^*$ transitions, the extinction coefficient (ε) ranges from 10 to 100 $M^{-1}cm^{-1}$, whereas allowed $\pi \rightarrow \pi^*$ transitions, the extinction coefficients range from 1000 to 100,000 $M^{-1}cm^{-1}$. As solvent polarity increases, $n \rightarrow \pi^*$ transitions tend to shift to shorter wavelengths. This shift is referred to as a hypsochromic, or blue shift. For many $\pi \rightarrow \pi^*$ transitions, an increase in polarity causes a shift to longer wavelengths, and this shift is known as a bathochromic, or red shift.

In this exercise you will model the $n \rightarrow \pi^*$ transition of acetone in the gas phase and obtain the calculated electronic spectrum using configuration interaction. The calculation will be repeated with solvent molecules surrounding acetone to simulate the solvent effect.

Gas Phase Spectrum

Build the acetone molecule. It will be easier to extract data if the CO bond is aligned with the y-axis. The CO lies on the secondary axis. Select Edit-Align Molecule and align the secondary axis with Y and the primary with Z. Optimize the structure using MM+ and save it.

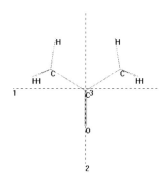

Set up a semi-empirical ZINDO/S calculation. Use the Options box to select Configuration Interaction using the Singly Excited Method and an Orbital Criterion of 5 for both occupied and unoccupied orbitals. Start a log file at Quantum Print Level = 0. Do a Single Point calculation. When it is completed, choose Electronic Spectrum from the Calculate menu to observe the spectrum. All possible transitions among the highest five occupied and lowest 5 unoccupied are shown on the upper part of the spectrum. The lower part of the spectrum shows the "allowed" transitions, i.e. those with oscillator strength greater than zero. The $n \rightarrow \pi^*$ transitions of acetone have a fairly low extinction coefficient (i.e. an oscillator strength near zero) and will not be observed as "allowed" in this method. Verify that the $n \rightarrow \pi^*$ transitions are those near 400 nm by visualizing the two highest occupied MOs to determine which is n and which is π. The lowest unoccupied MO is the π^*. Record values for both the singlet $\rightarrow$ singlet and singlet $\rightarrow$ triplet $n \rightarrow \pi^*$ transitions.

Polar Solvent Box

To simulate the effect of solvent we will surround the molecule with a box of water molecules and then select those within a 6Å radius of acetone to do the calculation. With the acetone molecule on the screen, choose Setup-Periodic Box as shown on the next page. You can leave the default options. After clicking OK, your acetone molecule will be surrounded in three dimensions with water molecules.

To eliminate water molecules that are not close and therefore to speed up the calculation, do the following. Set the selection tool to Molecules and check Select Sphere on the same menu. Select the acetone molecule. Once it is highlighted, place the cursor over the molecule and right-left drag a sphere of about 6Å. That is, press the right mouse button and then the left and drag while holding both buttons down. The status line will show the dimension of the sphere. When you release the buttons, some of the water molecules will be highlighted.

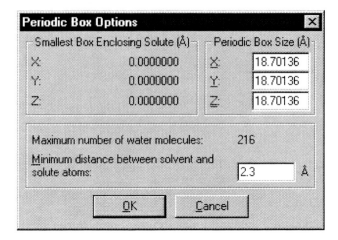

Next use the Select menu to check Complement Selection. This will un-select the ones near acetone and select the outer water molecules. Delete the outer water molecules. You should be left with acetone and its surrounding water molecules. Rotate the structures with the XY tool to be sure there are water molecules on all sides of the acetone. If there are not, you may want to try it again. Optimize the entire group of molecules using MM+ using a RMS convergence limit of 0.1. Be sure that nothing is selected when doing this.

Open a log file and do the ZINDO/S-CI calculation as before. Select the acetone molecule before starting the calculation. The calculation will be done on the selected molecule but the surrounding field will be "felt."

The transition from the highest occupied orbital is the one of interest. Record values for both the singlet → singlet and singlet → triplet transition for the solvated system. Determine how they have shifted relative to gas phase acetone.

Non-Polar Solvent Box

A box of chloroform or other nonpolar solvent can be made using a macro available on the HyperChem Web page. Download the self-extracting file solvent.zip from Excel Macros section of free software. Build the chloroform molecule and minimize it using MM+. Use the macro to build a box of molecules. The density of chloroform is 1.499

g/cm^3 so 484 molecules will be drawn in the 40x40x40 Å box. Modify the macro accordingly if you use a different solvent.

Merge the acetone and the box of chloroform. This will place acetone at the corner of the box. Translate the molecule to the center by selecting it and using Edit-Translate to move it to about 20,20,20, the center of the box.

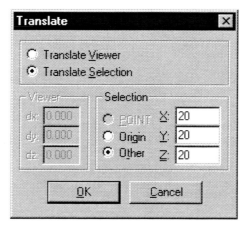

Select the acetone and its neighboring molecules as you did above to remove some of the solvent using a 6Å radius. Optimize the whole system using MM+.

Select acetone and do a single point ZINDO/S-CI calculation. When finished, view the electronic spectrum and record the information in the table.

Calculate the shifts in wave numbers for polar and non-polar solvents. Do they correspond to the kind of shifts observed experimentally?

Singlet and Triplet n → π* Transitions for Acetone

n → π*	Transition energy (nm)		Transition energy (cm⁻¹)	
	S → T	S → S	S → T	S → S
Gas				
Water				
Acetonitrile				
Chloroform				

Shifts Relative to Gas Phase

	Shift in cm⁻¹	
	S → T	S → S
Gas		
Water		
Acetonitrile		
Chloroform		

Reference

Gao, J. In *Reviews in Computational Chemistry;* Lipkowitz, K. B.;
Boyd, D. R. Eds.; VCH: New York, 1996; Volume 7, Chapter 3.

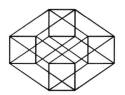

Chapter 8
Molecular Dynamics

Computing average properties of a chemical system is the goal of both molecular dynamics and Monte Carlo computation methods. A molecular dynamic simulation uses a classical method (i.e. Newtonian mechanics based on positions and momenta) to formulate the equations of motion of the system and computes a statistical mechanical description of the system (i.e. a semi-empirical or molecular mechanics method) as it changes. Molecular dynamics can be used to plot the changes in properties as the system evolves over time.

HyperChem implements two kinds of molecular dynamics computations. The first, simply called molecular dynamics, uses the classical second law equation of motion to compute the acceleration of each particle over time. Langevin dynamics adds terms to the acceleration calculation that can be varied to simulate frictional forcers (i.e. viscosity) or random factors (Brownian motion). It is important in simulation of systems in solutions.

45. Molecular Reaction Movies

As chemists we juggle many models of the life of a molecule in our heads. On the one hand is the strictly visual model of molecules bouncing into each other, reacting, rearranging, and eventually, producing new molecules. Superimposing some order on that are the rules we've learned in chemistry about the likely mechanisms and results of chemical reactions. Over all of that (some would say under it) is the quantum theory that should in principle be able to predict and explain the transition from initial to final state of a chemical system. We will attempt to tie those three pictures together in this lab.

The object will be to take chemical reactants, shoot them at each other to simulate a collision, and observe the outcome. The interactions of the reactants will be modeled by semi-empirical quantum theory using molecular dynamics to introduce time and energy into the system.

Setting up a reaction is a three-step process. The first step is to construct the reactant molecules and position them in a starting orientation. The second is to establish a direction of motion for one of the reactants so that the two reactants will collide in the proper orientation. Finally, the collision is set in motion and we use quantum mechanics to watch it evolve over time.

It is important to note in these simulations that when the simulation stops and rendering is changed back to sticks, the bond connections are not changed – they are unrelated to the quantum mechanical calculation and don't reflect the new bonding scheme. Distances between atoms do reflect the new system, as do the various angles.

S_N2 Reaction

In the first exercise you will examine an S_N2 reaction in which a reactant collides with another molecule, attaching itself and forcing elimination of another moiety. The example is the elimination Br^- from 2-bromobutane by attack of OH^-.

Construct 2-bromobutane and optimize its geometry using AM1 or PM3. On the same screen, construct an OH^- on the side away from the bromine. The O of the hydroxide ion should be between 5 and 10 Ångstroms from the carbon attached to the bromine. Orient the OH^- fragment like a spear aiming at the carbon holding the bromine.

Select the carbon atom holding the bromine and name that selection using the standard name POINT, then un-select it by L-clicking in the workspace.

Select the two atoms of the OH fragment. While these two are selected pull down the Setup menu and choose Set Velocity. In that dialog box, choose POINT for the direction and a magnitude of 100 for velocity. (This means that the OH will move toward the right. If it needs to move left, use -100 for velocity.) Un-select the OH.

Connect the O to the carbon attached to the bromine. Render the system in overlapping spheres. Choose AM1 or PM3 from the setup menu. In the options on the setup, set the charge to –1 and the multiplicity to 2.

On the Compute menu choose Molecular Dynamics. Set the heat and cool times to zero, a step size of 0.001 and the simulation time to about 0.2 ps. Use a simulation temperature of zero. Check restart and uncheck constant temperature. If you want to save the simulation, click on Snap Shots and name the file. Then Click Proceed.

You may have to re-center the system occasionally by pressing the space bar. When the system stops, change the rendering method to sticks by pressing F2. Notice that the bond connections have not changed. Remember, the distances reflect the new system, not the lines you have drawn. Measure the C-Br and the C-OH distances. How closely does the CO distance approximate a single bond? Have the angles around carbon changed? You may want to stop the simulation while it appears that both Br and OH are "attached" and measure the bond angles at that point.

Diels-Alder Reaction

The second example is the Diels-Alder addition of acrolein ($CHOCH=CH_2$) to cis-butadiene.

~10 A°

Build the two molecules separately and optimize each using AM1. Merge the two files and position the two molecules about 10-15 Å apart and aligned so that they present two parallel planes with the C=C of the acrolein roughly aligned with a line between the end carbon of butadiene.

With the select option set on atoms, select the uppermost butadiene carbon and the uppermost acrolein carbon in the C=C bond. You have created a line between the two carbons and should now name that selection using the predefined name LINE. Deselect the two atoms.

Select the entire acrolein molecule. While it is selected, pull down the setup menu and choose Set Velocity. In the dialog box, choose LINE for the direction and a magnitude of -100 for velocity assuming that acrolein is on the right. Un-select the acrolein.

Set the rendering method to overlapping spheres. Choose AM1 from the setup menu. The charge is zero and the multiplicity is 1.

Using the compute menu Molecular Dynamics option, enter the following time parameters: heat time to zero, simulation time to 0.25 ps, cool time to 0.1 ps, step size 0.001. Use temperature parameters as follows: simulation temperature =1000, final temperature=100, stepsize=50. Check restart and uncheck constant temperature. Then Proceed.

When the simulation stops, render the system in sticks. Click on various bonds to see that the former butadiene and acrolein double bonds are now nearer to single bond lengths and that the butadiene butadiene single bond is at a double bond length now.

46. Stability of Carbocations

Carbocations are know to be stable in the order tertiary > secondary > primary > methyl. The stability is explained by the ability of the alkyl groups attached to supply electrons to the positively charged carbon to diminish the charge. In the formation of cations from alcohols

$$R\text{-}OH \quad + \quad H^+ \quad \rightarrow \quad R^+ \quad + \quad H_2O$$

The rate-limiting step is the removal of the water. Once again, the rate of reaction favors the tertiary over the secondary over the primary. In this exercise you will investigate both the thermodynamic and kinetic aspects of carbocation formation.

You will examine the relative stability and ease of formation of primary, secondary and tertiary organic cations in three different ways. First, you will protonate alcohols and watch as the molecules release water over time. Second, you will calculate the heats of formation of carbocations. Third, you will compute the molecular energy as a function of reaction coordinates as water is removed from protonated alcohols.

Water Dissociating from Protonated Alcohols

To examine the relative stability of primary, secondary and tertiary alcohols, carry out the following "reactions" using HyperChem's PM3 semi-empirical method for each of the alcohols shown below.

Construct the alcohol with explicit hydrogens turned off. (Build the molecule and Add Hydrogens and ModelBuild.) Turn on explicit hydrogens and allow ions. Add a second hydrogen to the oxygen. Use Modelbuild to get the approximate bond length.

Optimize this structure using the PM3 semi-empirical method. Under Options, set charge = +1, spin multiplicity = 1 and SCF convergence = 0.0001. Save the optimized structure. This will serve as a starting point for each molecular dynamics run. Set the display to Overlapping Spheres

Set up a molecular dynamics simulation on the molecule with the conditions:

Heat and cool time	0 ps
Run time	0.5 ps
Simulation temperature	300
Step size	0.001 ps
In vacuo and constant temperature boxes checked.	

Initiate the run by L-clicking on Proceed. Note the time when the water molecule separates from the remainder of the molecule to leave the cation behind. If it fails to separate in the time simply record no separation. You can use the out-of-plane rotation tool during the simulation to better observe the protonated site.

Repeat at each higher temperature always starting from the optimized file that you saved. You can stop the simulation as soon as dissociation occurs. For each run note the time when the water molecule appears to separate from the remainder of the molecule leaving the cation behind or no if it fails to separate in 1 ps.

	500 K	1000 K	1500 K	2000 K
1-butanol				
2-butanol				
tert-butanol				

Heat of Reaction

Next, examine the enthalpy change for the reaction:

$$R\text{-}OH + H^+ \rightarrow R^+ + H_2O$$

Fill in the blanks of the table below. This requires running a geometry optimization on each alcohol and each cation and extracting the heat of formation from log file or using a script. Calculate the heat of reaction using Hess's Law.

	$\Delta_f H$ of alcohol (kcal/mol)	$\Delta_f H$ of proton (kcal/mol)	$\Delta_f H$ of the carbocation (kcal/mol)	$\Delta_f H$ of water (kcal/mol)	$\Delta_{rxn} H$ (kcal/mol)
1-butanol		367.20		68.38	
2-butanol		367.20		68.38	
tert-butanol		367.20		68.38	

Charges

For each of the optimized carbocations, note the charge on the sp^2 carbon.

Reaction Coordinate Diagram

Finally, look at what happens as one pulls the protonated alcohols apart. To carry out this calculation, start in each case with the optimized protonated alcohol used for earlier calculations. The technique will be to do a series of calculations with varying bond lengths of the C-O bond. The C-O bond distance will be fixed using restraints and the rest of the molecular geometry will be optimized. The process can be automated using an Excel macro to drive HyperChem using Dynamic Data Exchange. One creates a macro file that extracts a bond length from an Excel spreadsheet, passes it to HyperChem and tells HyperChem to do a geometry optimization. It then extracts the molecular energy from HyperChem and pastes it into the spreadsheet.

To use the spreadsheet as it stands, you must first, for each of the alcohols, start HyperChem, call in the protonated alcohol, select the C-O bond and name it using the predefined name LINE. De-select the bond. Start the Excel spreadsheet and click on the box that has the first bond length. Then start the macro.

After doing the bond length versus energy calculations for the three protonated alcohols in steps of 0.25 from 1.0 to 3.5 Ångstroms, plot all three sets of data and compare them.

Molecular Rearrangement

As a last calculation, attach a proton to 3-methyl-2-butanol. Run a molecular dynamics simulation for 1 ps at 2000 degrees. With any luck, you should see water dissociate and a hydride shift occur.

Excel Spreadsheet

Bond Length	Total Energy
1.00	
1.25	
1.50	
1.75	
2.00	
2.25	
2.50	
2.75	
3.00	

Excel Macro

Control-R	Compute.Results
Channel	=OpenFile()
	=IF(ISERROR(Channel))
	=RETURN()
	=END.IF()
	=EXECUTE(Channel,"[query-response-has-tag(no)]")
	=EXECUTE(Channel,"[calculation-method semi-empirical]")
	=EXECUTE(Channel,"[semi-empirical-method pm3]")
	=EXECUTE(Channel,"[quantum-total-charge 1]")
	=EXECUTE(Channel,"[multiplicity 1]")
	=WHILE(NOT(ISBLANK(SELECTION())))
Command	=EXECUTE(Channel,"[restraint LINE,"&SELECTION()&",10000.0]")
	=EXECUTE(Channel,"[do-optimization]")
	=FORMULA.ARRAY(REQUEST(Channel,"total-energy"),"rc[1]")
	=SELECT("r[1]c")
	=NEXT()
	=TERMINATE(Channel)
	=RETURN()
	OpenFIle
	=INITIATE("HyperChem","System")
	=RETURN(NewChan)

47. Conformation Searches with Molecular Dynamics

Quenched dynamics are simulations done at high temperature but constant total energy. The goal will be to generate conformers separated from the current structure by energy barriers too high to overcome with room temperature simulations. Sampling as much of phase space as possible does this. Equilibrium properties will not be calculated. Thus, slow heating and small time steps that help to maintain the system in a near-equilibrated state are not necessary. Larger time steps get the systems through phase space faster. High temperatures enable the system to overcome energy barriers. However, too large time steps or too rapid heating could result in excessive forces or unrealistic coordinates and should be avoided.

Overview of Method

A good starting molecule is 1,2-dichloroethane. We know that the anti-conformer is more stable than the gauche conformation. We'll start the simulation in the latter conformation and see if it can get out of the potential well. Short runs (0.5-1ps) at high temperature (6000-1200K) are usually enough to overcome rotational barriers.

Draw and modelbuild the gauche isomer of 1,2-dichloroethane. (Cl-C-C-Cl torsion = 60.) Setup a MM+ calculation. Since we will be interested in that torsion angle, name it by selecting the four atoms and choosing Select-Name Selection. Call it Torsion.

From the Compute menu choose Molecular Dynamics and set the parameters as shown in the table below. Note that if constant temperature is not checked, the simulation is done at constant energy.

Once you've set up the simulation parameters, use the Averages button to open the another dialog box and select the properties to be averaged. This box is shown on the next page.

Click on up to four items on the list and click Add. Notice that they move to the center section. You can graph and average the properties by again clicking and moving them to the right most section. The properties are Kinetic energy (EKIN), potential energy (EPOT), total energy (ETOT) and Temperature (TEMP). The letter D in front of these symbols indicates that the RMS deviation from the mean would be reported. Notice that the Name Torsion appears on the list. That is the one you named!

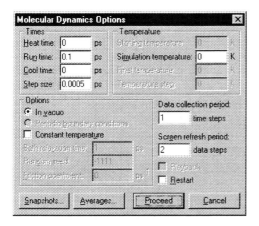

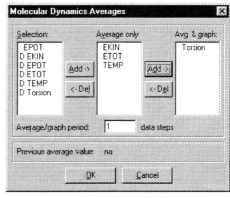

In the example shown, the total energy and the kinetic energy, total energy, temperature and torsion would be calculated and the graphs would show how the torsion changes.

Once everything is ready to go, click Proceed to run the simulation. Or, you can start a snapshot file if you want to playback the simulation. This is very useful, as it is possible to obtain additional averages or graphs from each playback. HyperChem will prompt you to name the file containing the snapshots if you make that selection. Move the graph-averages screen to the side so you can watch the motion. You can move the molecule using the regular xy rotation tool during the simulation. This only alters the view, not the molecular coordinates.

To find a property average, click on the item in the Compute-Molecular Dynamics-Averages box. The value will appear on the Previous Average value line. If you have named the molecular system (i.e. a *.hin exists) the averages are computed after each step and stored in a file of the same name but with the extension .csv. If you have not previously named the molecular system, the averages are in the file chem.scr in the current working directory. This file is stored in a comma-delimited format that could be imported into a spreadsheet.

Varying the Simulation Parameters

These runs are short and ideal for getting a feel for the effect of changing parameters. Is a heating step necessary for a non-equilibrium simulation such as this? See what happens if you shorten or omit it. Omit the cool time; this leaves you with a shorter run. Or, double the run time and see what happens when the system has more time to explore phase space. Vary the time step and note the effect on

DETOT/ETOT. For small enough steps (about 0.0005 ps) the simulation should run at close to constant energy.

The table shows suggested variations but you may wish to try others. It's helpful to use a table of setup parameters and calculated properties. In addition, you may wish to include graphs like the one reproduced here. It's easy to paste these images into application programs from HyperChem. Before running a simulation, set up HyperChem's image copier to do what you want. Under Edit choose Setup Image: specify Top Level as the window to be copied, Metafile as the file format and Clipboard as the destination. After the run is complete, use the F9 key to capture the graph window to the clipboard. Then you can paste it into a word processor or other applications program in the usual manner.

From the graph, it is apparent that there was considerable motion, but a transition to the trans- structure did not occur. In fact, the average value of the torsion was 70°.

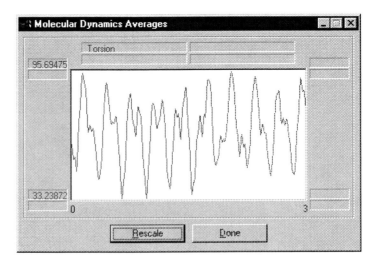

High Temperature, Longer Run Time

At this point some information on the height of the barrier to rotation would be useful. We can use this to choose an appropriate simulation temperature.

If room temperature (300K) corresponds to 0.6 kcal/mol, and the gauche-trans barrier is close to 4 kcal/mol, then a molecule needs more than 1800K to overcome this barrier. Too high temperature could result in broken bonds however. Since large temperature fluctuations occur in our simulations, we anticipate that a reasonable high temperature of 800 or 1200 K will permit rotational transitions without rupturing a bond.

Try a run time of 800 K and a run time of 2 ps. Monitor both the Cl-C-

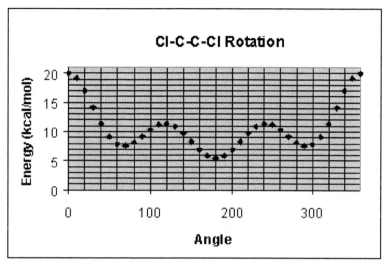

C-H torsion and an H-C-C-Cl torsion.   This trajectory found and remained in the potential energy well corresponding to torsion values of ±180°, the trans conformer. Unfortunately, the torsion angle convention results in an awkward graph. The trans region lies at the top and bottom of the graph.

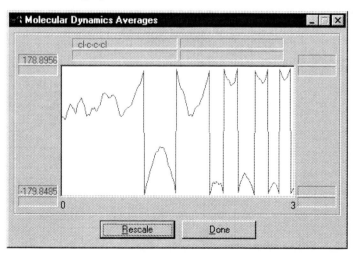

Notice however that the H-C-C-Cl graph shows the conformational transition more clearly than the Cl-C-C-Cl graph at the end.

Comments and Suggestions for Further Work

Don't use time steps greater than 0.001 ps. Possible consequences include large forces and non-conservation of energy.

Use small molecules whose barriers you know from experiment. Note, HyperChem doesn't know the experimental barriers. It's more in touch with the MM+ values. See the dihedral driver lab (see Exercise #23) for a table of experimental barriers to rotation and a fast way to generate rotational potential energy curves.

At high temperatures, there is more motion so the time step should be shortened.

Try systems with low barriers for fast runs. Use lower temperatures. Try to trap the system in one conformer, by clicking Done and Cancel. Then run at higher temperature until transitions, and finally, free-rotation, occurs.

Setup Parameter	Run 1	Run 2 Omit heating	Run 3 Omit cooling	Run 4 Double run time	Run 5 Change time step
Heat time	1 ps		1 ps	1 ps	1 ps
Run time	1 ps	1 ps	1 ps	2 ps	1 ps
Cool time	1 ps	1 ps		1 ps	1 ps
Step Size	0.0005 ps	0.0005 ps	0.0005 ps	0.0005 ps	0.001 ps
Start T	300 K	300 K	300 K	300 K	300 K
Simulation Temp	400 K	400 K	400 K	400 K	400 K
Final T	300 K	300 K	300 K	300 K	300 K
Temp step	30 K	30 K	30 K	30 K	30 K
Constant	Energy	Energy	Energy	Energy	Energy

Check "In Vacuo" for constant energy.

Averages	Run 1	Run 2	Run 3	Run 4	Run 5
D ETOT					
ETOT					
D TEMP					
TEMP					
TORSION					
E KIN					
E POT					
DEKIN					

48. Simulated Annealing

Conformational barrier height can be surmounted in molecular dynamics simulations by increasing the simulation temperature. During such a dynamics run, snapshots can be taken for later optimization to generate a set of stable conformers for complex structures. Slow cooling (annealing) can then be used to locate a more stable (possibly global) minimum on the potential energy surface.

Build and optimize a structure of interest. Use one of the following for a fast first run:

Ethane	1,2-dichloroethane
Acetone	Butane
N-methyl acetamide	Alanine dipeptide.

Select and name any molecular feature that you wish to monitor during the dynamics run. These could include torsions, bond angles or bond lengths. Choose a starting conformation for the dynamics run that is stable but not the most stable conformer. Make a note of the rotational barrier to the global minimum, if known. Set up the calculation to average and graph the named selections, temperature and total energy. More than four features produce a cluttered graph however. Set up a snapshot file so that you can replay the simulation for further analysis. Note the parameters used in each run. Run the simulation and record the average values of the selected quantities. Then vary the parameters and re-run.

Parameter	In general	This lab
Heat time	0 to 1 ps	0.1 to 2 ps
Run time	0 to 1000 ps	2 to 5
Cool time	0 to 10 ps	0.1 to 2
Step size	0.0005 to 0.001 for explicit H 0.001 to 0.001 for united atom force fields	0.005 to 0.001

Solvent Effects

To test the effect of water as a solvent, go back to the setup menu and choose Periodic Box. You must set the size of the box: double the size of the smallest box is a reasonable choice. The program will fill the box with TIP3P models of water thermally equilibrated at 300 K and one atmosphere pressure. Optimize the system as usual and note the time required. If you choose to do a dynamics run on this system, each time step will take about this long.

N-methylacetamide

The graph below shows the O-C-N-C torsion during a 1 ps heat, 3 ps run and finally a 1 ps cool down. MM+ was used for the calculation. Notice that during the heating, the selected torsion varied over only about ±35° from the planar conformation even at 500 K. In the end (the cooling) it settled down to a stable conformation.

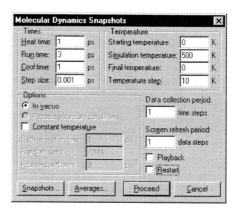

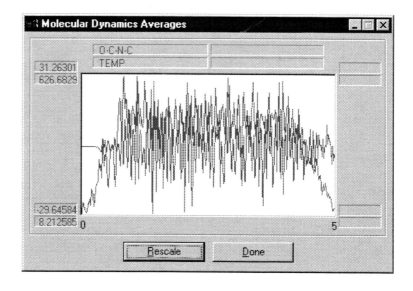

The average value for the selected torsion angle was about 0.37°. Think about this in terms of the partial multiple bond character that might be expected for the C-N bond.

If you saved the snapshot file, you can easily see how that length varied during the simulation. Compare its average value with the molecular mechanics (MM+) modeled C-N single bond and the C=N double bond values of about 1.47 and 1.32Å respectively.

You can stop a playback at any point and minimize the geometry while the system is in a particular conformation.

Trifluoromethyl Phenol

Recent *ab initio* studies of trifluoromethyl suggest possible intramolecular hydrogen bonding occurs. Try a molecular dynamics simulation and simulated annealing using MM+ to determine an optimum conformation of this molecule.

Draw and modelbuild the structure. Name the torsions: H-O-C-C and F-C-C-C using Select-Name Selection. Set up an MM+ calculation. Start a molecular dynamics calculation using the settings shown. Save a snapshot file so you can explore other values as well. Select the two named torsions to be graphed and averaged.

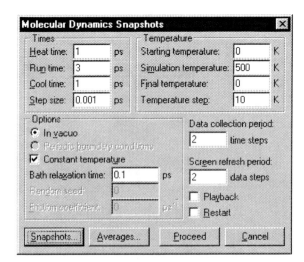

Use the graph to determine the average torsion angles which show how the –OH group and the CF_3 group are oriented relative to the plane of the ring. How far apart are the H and F in the final structure? Is this close enough to be considered a hydrogen bond?

The authors indicate that hydrogen bonding is assisted by resonance as shown below. What bonds would you need to monitor to see if such structures occurred during the simulation? Try it out using the playback file.

Reference

Kovacs, A.; Kolossvary, I.; Csonka, G. L.; Hargittai, I. *J. Comp. Chem.* **1996**, 17, 1804-1819.

49. Langevin Dynamics

If you tried the molecular dynamics simulation of a molecule in a solvent box you realize that the calculation is very time-consuming. There is another way to simulate the effects of solvent molecules that is considerably faster! Langevin dynamics does this by adding a random force to the calculation to simulate the effect of collisions and of solvent viscosity.

In this exercise we will compare two methods: Molecular dynamics and Langevin dynamics on the same system. Let's pick a simple molecule such as acetic acid.

Molecular Dynamics

Draw and optimize the molecule using MM+. Select and name the O-C-O-H torsion. Distort the molecule by setting this torsion at about 30° to begin the simulation. Use Edit-Set Bond torson while the four atoms are selected. Run a molecular dynamics simulation using the settings shown at the right.

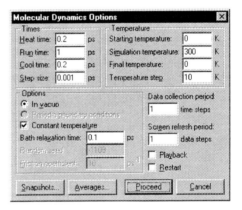

Follow the temperature and the named torsion during the simulation. Save a snapshot file if you want to playback the simulation later.

Save the graph produced so you can compare it to the one you will generate using Langevin Dynamics. Making the graph the active screen and pressing Alt-PrintScreen on the keyboard can do this. This copies to active window to clipboard. Then paste it into a word processing document.

Langevin Dynamics

Using the same starting conformation of acetic acid, choose Langevin Dynamics from the compute menu. Notice that some new options need to be set to start the simulation, the random seed and the friction coefficient. The former can be left at the default value: it is the seed for the random number generator. The friction coefficient is used in the motion equation both to simulate the solvent viscosity and random thermal motions of the solvent. At zero, the simulation is basically the same as the molecular dynamics. At higher values the motion is diffusion like. See the HyperChem Reference manuals for specifics about the settings. We will use 10 here. Smart used this value to simulate the alanine dipeptide in water. If you have time, explore how varying this setting changes the simulation.

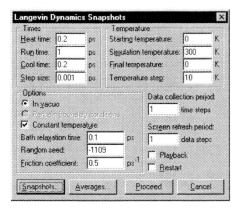

Save the graph of O-C-O-H torsion as you did before. Compare the two techniques. How does addition of the friction change the movement?

Reference

Smart, J. L.; Marrone, T. J. McCammon, J. A. *J Comp. Chem.;* **1997**, 18, 1750-1759.

50. Intramolecular Vibrations

While HyperChem allows full modeling of the infrared spectrum of a molecule and animation of the vibrations via the Compute-Vibrational Spectrum menu, one can also use molecular dynamics to focus on the oscillation of a particular bond or set of bonds during a dynamics simulation. In this exercise you will observe how frequency of oscillation changes as a function of mass. In the second part the changes that occur as the temperature increases will be investigated.

Vibration Frequency and Mass

Draw and model build four halogen-substituted methane molecules: CH_3F, CH_3Cl, CH_3Br and CH_3I. Optimize each using AM1. Use an SCF convergence limit of 1e-5. Select the C-X bond and name the selection using the default value, LINE.

Set up a molecular dynamics simulation using zero for the heat and cool times and a 0.5 ps run time. Use room temperature, 300K, for the simulation temperature. Save the snapshot file using an appropriate name. Choose Averages and move LINE to the average & graph box as shown below. Then Proceed.

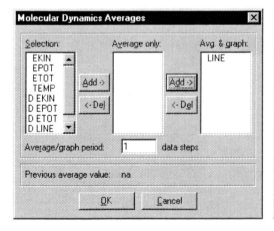
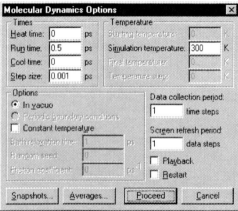

When the graph is complete, capture it to the clipboard (ALT-PrintScreen or Edit-CopyImage) and paste it into a word processor.

Count the number of oscillation cycles the molecule undergoes during the 0.5 picosecond interval and record the number in the table. Try to estimate fractions if reasonable.   Use Playback to review the simulation is necessary.

	Experimental Frequency (cm^{-1})	Oscillations per 0.5 ps	Average Bond Distance (Å)
CH_3F			
CH_3Cl			
CH_3Br			
CH_3I			

Temperature Dependence of Oscillation

The hydrogen halides provide simple systems to study as a function of temperature. Change the Run Time to 0.1 ps and use the simulation temperatures in the table. Set up the Averages to graph the bond distance. It will make counting peaks easier if you start each simulation from the optimized geometry. Record the number of oscillations per time period and the range of bond lengths at each temperature.

Move the graph to the side so you can watch the motion of the molecule. Write down any observations that you notice if changes occur as the temperature increases. I.e., does rotational motion increase as well as vibrational motion?

How does the frequency of oscillation change during the simulation? How does the amplitude change during the simulation?   Explain your results.

50. Intramolecular Vibrations

Temperature	Oscillations per 0.1 ps	Range High Value	Range Low Value	Amplitude Change
100				
300				
500				
800				
1000				
2000				
3000				

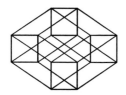

Chapter 9
Teaching Notes and Results

Integrating molecular modeling across the chemistry curriculum is a real challenge. I have included suggested courses only to show that there is a place for modeling across the traditional curriculum. The choice of text book influences what may or may not be covered in a specific course. Further, the division of the undergraduate chemistry curriculum into general, organic, analytical, physical, etc. may change as various new initiatives supported by NSF take hold. In addition to courses in the chemistry-major curriculum, some of these might be used in non-major courses.

The results of some of the exercises are included so instructors will have some idea of the accuracy of calculations obtained using the settings suggested in the exercises. As mentioned in the introduction, sometimes gradients and SCF controls have been set at levels so results will be obtained in shorter time periods. "Research quality" results would require longer time than might typically be available in a one or two hour lab period.

Suggested Courses

1.	Building Small Molecules	Gen, Inorg, Org, Bio
2.	Visualizing Structure and Charge Distribution	Gen
3.	Stereoisomers: Carvone and Hexahelicene	Org
4.	The Steroid Nucleus and Cholesterol	Bio
5.	Alkaloids: Acetylcholine Impersonators	Bio
6.	Polypeptides and Proteins	Bio
7.	Nucleotides: DNA and RNA Mutation	Bio
8.	Building Coordination Complexes	Gen, Inorg
9.	Periodicity: Bond Lengths and Bond Angles	Gen, Inorg
10.	VSEPR and Dipole Moments	Gen
11.	Ionization Energy	Org, Inorg, PChem
12.	Proton Affinity	Org, Inorg, Anal
13.	Electron Affinity	Inorg
14.	Periodicity of Bond Enthalpy	Gen
15.	Structure-Stability Relationships...Crown Ether Complexes	Inorg
16.	The Acidity of Oxoacids	Gen, Anal
17.	Exploring the Formation of Molecular Orbitals –1	PChem, Gen
18.	Exploring the Formation of Molecular Orbitals –2	PChem
19.	Fragment Molecular Orbitals: Ethene and Formaldehyde	PChem
20.	Walsh Diagrams for H_2X Molecules	PChem, Inorg
21.	The Jahn-Teller Effect	Inorg
22.	Small Molecules Conformation Analysis by Hand	Org
23.	Small Molecules Conformation Analysis Using Macros	Org
24.	Torsion Barriers: Methyl and Phenyl	Org
25.	The Peptide Bond	Bio
26.	Stable Conformers of the Alanine Dipeptide	Bio
27.	The Inversion Barrier in Ammonia and Aniline	Org

Results

8. Building Coordination Complexes

Version 5.1 of HyperChem includes transitional metal parameters that produced the results shown here starting from the "modelbuild" geometry.

Complex		M to axial-ligand distance (Å)	M to equitorial-ligand distance (Å)	Angles (°)
Copper	(Lit.)	(2.296)	(2.391)	(90, 120)
	Calc'd.	2.27	2.31	90, 120
Nickel	(Lit.)	(2.17)	(1.87)	(All 90) ax-M-eq 96.54
	Calc'd.	2.22	1.91	eq-M-eq 89.24

Single point ZINDO/1calculations give the following energies for the "modelbuild" structures using the literature values for the bond lengths indicated above. Minimization using ZINDO takes a very long time!

	C_{4v}	D_{3h}
$Ni(CN)_5^{3-}$	-2834.2 kcal/mol	-2843.1 kcal/mol
$CuCl_5^{3-}$	-2775.6 kcal/mol	-2788.7 kcal/mol

9. Periodicity: Bond Lengths and Bond Angles

Bond Lengths in (Å)

Molecule	Bond Length	Model builder	MM+	AM1	PM3	Exp.
CH_3-CH_2-CH_3	C-C	1.54	1.53	1.51	1.51	1.53
CH_3-O-CH_3	C-O	1.43	1.41	1.42	1.41	1.42
CH_3-S-CH_3	C-S	1.74	1.82	1.75	1.80	1.81
CH_3-Se-CH_3	C-Se	1.93	1.95	na	1.95	1.94
SCl_2	S-Cl	2.01	2.01	1.96	2.0	2.01
$SeCl_2$	Se-Cl	2.15	2.15	na	2.16	2.16
OCl_2	O-Cl	1.72	1.65	1.73	1.70	1.70
OF2	O-F	1.45	1.38	1.35	1.38	1.42
H_2O	O-H	0.96	0.94	0.96	0.95	0.96
H_2S	S-H	1.34	1.34	1.32	1.29	1.35
H_2Se	Se-H	1.48	1.47	na	1.47	1.46
PF_3	P-F	1.78	1.78	1.54	1.56	1.56
PCl_3	P-Cl	2.05	2.05	1.92	2.06	2.04
PBr_3	P-Br	2.20	2.20	2.10	2.15	2.22
PI_3	P-I	2.39	2.39	2.25	2.36	2.46

Bond Angles in Degrees

Molecule	Bond Angle	Model builder	MM+	AM1	PM3	Exp.
$CH_3-CH_2-CH_3$	C-C-C	109.47	111.69	112.16	111.77	109.5
CH_3-O-CH_3	C-O-C	109.47	112.68	112.89	114.11	112
CH_3-S-CH_3	C-S-C	109.47	99.33	102.74	102.52	99.1
$CH_3-Se-CH_3$	C-Se-C	120	96.09	na	100.80	96.2
SCl_2	Cl-S-Cl	109.47	92.10	106.31	101.58	102.8
$SeCl_2$	Cl-Se-Cl	120	90.69	na	99.60	99.6
OCl_2	Cl-O-Cl	109.47	104.52	111.06	109.23	110.8
OF_2	F-O-F	109.47	104.51	102.54	100.97	103.2
H_2O	H-O-H	109.47	104.48	103.53	107.63	104.5
H_2S	H-S-H	109.47	92.10	95.50	93.51	92.3
H_2Se	H-Se-H	120	90.60	na	93.57	91.0
PF_3	F-P-F	109.47	93.29	98.01	95.84	97.8
PCl_3	Cl-P-Cl	109.47	93.30	105.43	99.70	100.3
PBr_3	Br-P-Br	109.47	93.30	106.78	101.34	101.5
PI_3	I-P-I	109.47	93.29	107.50	107.36	102.0

Testing Other Trends

Molecule	Angle	AM1	STO-3G	6-31G**	Exp. (°)
PH_3	H-P-H	96.46	93.66	95.41	93.3
PF_3	F-P-F	98.01	94.58		97.8
NH_3	H-N-H	109.09	104.16	107.18	106.7
NF_3	F-N-F	102.63	102.16		102.2

Molecule	AM1	STO-3G	6-31G**	Exp.
OCl_2	111.06	109.33		110.9
OH_2	107.63	99.98	105.50	104.5
OF_2	102.54	102.44		103.1

10. Valence Shell Electron Repulsion Theory

This exercise presents several levels of investigation. Use of the model builder will give the correct "idealized" geometry about the central atom although not necessarily the correct arrangement of lone pairs according to VSEPR. The energy of the structure is determined using a single point calculation.   If students then rearrange the lone pair to an alternate position and invoke the modelbuilder, a new structure will be obtained for which the single-point energy can be computed. The correct VSEPR structure will have the lowest energy (i.e. most negative).

A second level of investigation uses a semi-empirical method to optimize the structure. AM1 or PM3 seem to have the most parameters for main groups elements. The results below were obtained using AM1 starting from the minimum energy arrangement from modelbuilder.

Table 1. Representative Compounds for VSEPR Study

Molecule	#Valence Electron Pairs	#Lone Pairs	Geometry of Orbitals	Predicted Best Structure	AM1 Single Point Energy (kcal/mol)	AM1 Optimized Energy (kcal/mol)
BeF_2	2	0		linear	-237.7	-249.6
BF_3	3	0		planar	-346.9	-464.6
NH_3	4	1		pyramidal	-276.4	-276.6
PH_3	4	1		pyramidal	-213.8	-221.7
CH_4	4	0		tetrahedral	-387.3	-388.1
H_2O	4	2		angular	-222.3	-223.0
H_2S	4	2		angular	-166.3	-169.4

SF_4 (2) LP – eq	5	1		see-saw	-301.6	-367.5
SF LP - ax					-307.1	-363.1
ClF_5	6	1		sq-based pyramid	-19.2	-30.5
SF_6	6	0		octahedral	-407.5	-510.5
ClF_3 () LP eq-eq	5	2		T-shaped	-49.7	-65.5
ClF_3 LP eq-ax					-4.79	-65.5
ClF_3 LP ax-ax					-64.4	-65.5
I_3^- (3) LP eq-eq-eq	5	3		linear	-118.5	-118.9
I_3^- LP eq-eq-ax					- 77.2	-118.9
I_3^- LP ax-eq-ax					- 97.5	-118.9
BrF_4^- (2) LP ax-ax	6	2		Square planar	-167.6	-168.1
  LP ax-eq					-84.9	-111.0

Geometry – Literature and AM1 for compounds in Table 1

Molecule	Predicted Best Structure	E-X Literature (Å)	E-X AM1 (Å)	X-E-X Literature (°)	X-E-X AM1 (°)
BeF$_2$		na	1.49	na	180
BF$_3$	planar	1.31	1.31	120	120
NH$_3$	pyramidal	1.012	0.998	106.7	109.1
PH$_3$	pyramidal	1.42	1.36	~93.5	96.4
CH$_4$	tetrahedral	1.10	1.11	109.5	109.47
H$_2$O	angular	0.96	0.961	104.5	103.6
H$_2$S	angular	1.35	1.32	92.3	95.5
SF$_4$	see-saw		SF$_{ax}$ 1.57 SF$_{eq}$ 1.57	a-S-e 101.4 a-S-a 173	a-S-e 87.9 a-S-a 170.3
ClF$_3$		ClF$_{ax}$ 1.7 ClF$_{eq}$ 1.6	1.68	87.5	120 (all)
ClF$_5$	trigonal bipyramid		Cl-F$_{ax}$ 1.67 Cl-F$_{eq}$ 1.69		a-Cl-e 105 e-Cl-e 86.1
SF$_6$	octahedral	1.58	1.54	90	90
I$_3^-$	linear	2.93	2.62	180	180
BrF$_4^-$	Square planar	1.88	1.84	90	90

Table 2. Dipole Moments

Compound	Experimental Dipole Moment, μ in Debyes	AM1 Dipole Moment, μ in Debyes
BeF_2	Not stable in gas phase	0
BF_3	0	0
NH_3	1.007	1.847
PH_3	2.292	2.293
CH_4	0	0
H_2O	1.85	1.86
H_2S		1.86
ClF_3	0.6	0.98
SF_4	0.632	2.13
SeF_4	1.78	No AM1 parameters
PCl_5	0.9	0
PF_5	0	0
ClF_5	0.55	
PCl_3	0.78	0
PBr_3	0.5	1.07
SF_6	0	0

11. Ionization Energy

Organic Compounds

	IP (eV)	−ε HOMO (eV)	ΔE
1,2,3,4-tetramethylbenzene	8.16	9.02	0.86
Methoxybenzene	8.20	9.11	0.91
1,4-diethylbenzene	8.40	9.12	0.72
1,3 diethylbenzene	8.49	9.28	0.79
Ethylbenzene	8.77	9.46	0.64
Phenylacetalide	8.82	9.40	0.58
Toluene	8.83	9.44	0.61
Bromobenzene	9.00	9.81	0.81
1,4 difluorobenzene	9.16	9.87	0.71
Benzene	9.24	9.75	0.51
1,2,3,5-tetrafluorobenzene	9.55	10.38	0.83
2-fluorobenzonitrile	9.78	10.22	0.44
4-cyanobenzoic acid	10.00	10.46	0.46

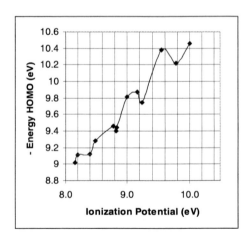

Inorganic Compounds

	IP (eV)	$-\varepsilon$ HOMO (eV)	ΔE
Phosphorus trichloride, PCl_3	9.90	10.63	0.79
Carbon disulfide, CS_2	10.07	9.38	-0.69
Ammonia, NH_3	10.07	10.42	0.35
Hydrogen iodide, HI	10.39	10.91	0.52
Hydrogen sulfide, H_2S	10.46	9.49	-0.97
Boron trichloride, BCl_3	11.60	12.32	0.70
Oxygen, O_2	12.07	10.49	-1.58
Ozone, O_3	12.53	13.10	0.57
Water, H_2O	12.62	12.46	-0.16
Hydrogen chloride, HCl	12.74	12.33	-0.41
Carbon dioxide, CO_2	13.78	13.21	-0.57
Carbon monoxide, CO	14.01	13.31	-0.70
Hydrogen fluoride, HF	16.03	14.09	-1.94

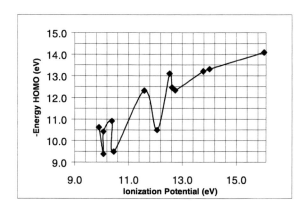

12. Proton Affinities

All energies in kcal/mol.

Compound	$\Delta_f H$ B (experiment)	$\Delta_f H$ BH+ (experiment)	$\Delta_f H$ B (AM1)	$\Delta_f H$ BH+ (AM1)
Pyridine	33	178	31.9	184.0
2-CH$_3$	23.7	164	25.5	173.7
2-CN	67	225	67.8	228.2
2-Cl	25	176	26.2	181.6
2-NO$_2$			42.7	209.0
2-OCH$_3$	-5.7	135	-5.88	145.1

Compound	ESP Minimum	Proton Affinity Calculated (kcal/mol)	Proton Afinity Experimental (kcal/mol)
2-NO$_2$	-0.142	200.9	
2-CN	-0.155	206.8	207.1 ± 1.6
2-Cl	-0.166	211.8	213.7 ± 1.6
Pyridine	-0.179	215.1	219.2 ± 1.7
2-OCH$_3$	-0.170	216.2	220.1 ± 1.7
2-CH$_3$	-0.186	219.0	222.7± 2.0

13. Electron Affinity

AM1 Energy Calculations

Molecule	$\Delta_f H$ neutral molecule (kcal/mol)	$\Delta_f H$ anion (kcal/mol)	Electron Affinity (eV)	$\Delta_f H$ neutral molecule, Experiment (kcal/mol)	EA Experiment (eV)
CO	-5.69	11.54	-0.71	-26.42	1.37
CS [1]	+94.83	76.78	+0.82	+67.00	1.6, 0.2
CO_2 [1]	-79.85	-37.90	-1.75	-94.05	-1.6, -0.6
CS_2	+17.46	12.98	+0.23	+27.95	0.512
COS	-28.98	-41.23	+0.57	-33.08	0.461
SO_2	-47.03	-83.26	+1.63	-70.94	1.1
NO	+1.19	+24.37	-0.97	+21.58	0.026
BCl_3	-97.09	-132.69	+1.53	-96.31	0.33±0.20
PF_3	-228.96	-200.73	-1.13	-229.07	-1.0
PCl_3	-89.10	-138.20	+2.11	-69.00	0.82±0.10
PBr_3	-23.39	-96.52	+3.29	-34.90	1.59±0.15

(1) The NIST Webbook gives two considerably different values.

14. Periodicity of Bond Enthalpies

All energies in kcal/mol

Group IIIA	Group IVA	Group V A	Group VI A	Group VII A
	CH 98.5	NH 93.5	HO 110.7	HF 136
AlH 67	SiH 77.2	PH 76.7	HS 80.9	HCl 103.2
GaH	GeH 69.1	AsH 71.0	HSe 74.6	HBr 87.5
InH 67±5	SnH 60.5	SbH 61.4	HTe 63.8	HI 71.5

15. Structure-Stability Relationships

I use this exercise to introduce the calculations of molecular mechanics in a sophomore Inorganic Chemistry course. The students have sufficient background in Physics and Calculus to understand the kind of calculations being done. It provides a tool for discussing the various kinds of energy calculated in molecular mechanics.

It takes considerable length of time to find "global minima" starting from scratch so the structures were provided to students so they could concentrate on the calculations and the relationships between computed energies and experimental values. An article by Glendening recently reported structures obtained from *ab initio* calculations. These make a good starting point for the alkali metal complexes.

Free Crown	D_{3d}	It is said to predominate in polar solvents.
Li	S_6	"folded...almost fully encloses cation."
K	D_{3d}	
Na	D_{3d}	
Rb	C_{3v}	
Cs	C_{3v}	

The alkaline earth complexes were modeled using geometries found for the alkali metals of similar size. Molecular dynamics runs followed by optimizations were used to find minimum energy structures.

Parameters

Modification of the parameter files was done based on literature values found for the potassium complex. Others were estimated. They should not be considered "research quality." They work for this experiment to illustrate the relationships the author wanted to show.

Additional References

Glendening, E. D.; Feller, D.; Thompson, M. A. *J. Am. Chem. Soc.* **1994,** 116, 10657-10669.

Ab initio studies of the alkali metal 18-crown-6 complexes

Hancock, R. D. *Acc. Chem. Res.* **1990**, 23, 253-257.

Reference to other cyclic ligands.

Hay, B. P. *Coord. Chem Reviews,* **1993**, 126, 177-236.

References to molecular mechanics applications in coordination chemistry

Molecule	Total Energy	Stretch	Bend	Torsion	VdW	Radius (pm)	Log K water	Log K water/ MeOH
Crown	17.88	0.67	5.49	-2.69	12.79			
Mg-18c6	48.66	0.70	16.83	21.68	6.84	72		
Li-18c6	54.51	1.63	11.77	22.82	15.66	76		
Ca-18c6	31.07	0.61	9.89	2.90	15.78	100	0.50	2.51
Na-18c6	32.62	0.54	10.33	6.43	13.22	102	0.80	2.76
Sr-18c6	25.57	0.68	7.15	-1.36	17.33	118	2.72	5.00
Ba-18c6	22.29	0.59	5.88	-1.83	16.00	136	3.87	6.00
K-18c6	22.25	0.52	5.79	-1.81	16.10	138	2.03	4.33
Rb-18c6	26.25	1.26	8.32	-0.83	15.67	152	1.56	3.46
Cs-18c6	33.37	1.30	10.19	0.44	19.47	1667	0.99	2.84

16. The Acidity of Oxoacids

Results of correlations suggested and tested by students using a linear least squares fit of specified parameters.

Function	R^2 Halogen Set	R^2 Extended Set
Partial Charge on E of Acid (δ_{Ea})	0.79	0.12
Partial Charge on O in acid (δ_{Oa})	0.10	0.03
Partial Charge on H in acid (δ_{Ha})	0.61	0.37
$(\delta_{Ea} - \delta_{Oa}) / r$ where r is O-H distance	0.87	0.19
Change in partial charge on central element on ionization $(\delta_{Ea} - \delta_{Eb})$	0.82	0.13
Ratio of charge on E to charge on O in acid $(\delta_{Ea} / \delta_{Oa})$	0.92	0.61
(δ_H / δ_{Ob}) + # oxo groups	0.93	0.92

One or two acids were the problem in most cases very poor correlation existed. This can give rise to valuable discussions related why the tested models failed in some cases.

20. Walsh Diagrams

H_2O

Angle	Core-core Energy	Electronic Energy	Binding Energy	Orbital Energy					
				-4	-3	-2	-1	0	1
90	4082.34	-16025.74	-290.72	-39.83	-19.76	-18.10	-16.45	7.53	7.68
95	4073.04	-16018.81	-293.10	-39.70	-20.05	-17.87	-16.41	7.36	7.95
100	4064.86	-16011.99	-294.45	-39.56	-20.31	-17.63	-16.36	7.19	8.22
105	4057.64	-16005.16	-294.85	-39.41	-20.55	-17.37	-16.29	7.00	8.50
110	4051.26	-15998.26	-294.32	-39.26	-20.76	-17.11	-16.21	6.80	8.79
115	4045.63	-15991.24	-292.93	-39.11	-20.94	-16.84	-16.11	6.59	9.07
120	4040.65	-15984.07	-290.75	-38.94	-21.09	-16.56	-15.99	6.38	9.36
125	4036.26	-15976.79	-287.85	-38.77	-21.21	-16.28	-15.86	6.17	9.65
130	4032.41	-15969.42	-284.33	-38.59	-21.30	-16.01	-15.71	5.96	9.93
135	4029.04	-15962.02	-280.31	-38.40	-21.36	-15.73	-15.54	5.75	10.22
140	4026.11	-15954.71	-275.93	-38.20	-21.39	-15.46	-15.36	5.56	10.50
145	4023.60	-15947.61	-271.34	-38.00	-21.40	-15.21	-15.17	5.37	10.77
150	4021.47	-15940.88	-266.74	-37.80	-21.38	-14.98	-14.97	5.20	11.03
155	4019.70	-15934.70	-262.32	-37.61	-21.35	-14.79	-14.76	5.06	11.27
160	4018.28	-15929.26	-258.31	-37.43	-21.30	-14.61	-14.58	4.93	11.48
165	4017.19	-15924.78	-254.92	-37.28	-21.26	-14.46	-14.43	4.84	11.66
170	4016.41	-15921.43	-252.34	-37.16	-21.22	-14.34	-14.33	4.77	11.80
175	4015.95	-15919.36	-250.73	-37.08	-21.19	-14.27	-14.26	4.72	11.88
180	4015.80	-15918.66	-250.18	-37.06	-21.18	-14.24	-14.24	4.71	11.91

The electronic energy alone is not necessarily a good measure of relative stability for strained systems. The electronic energy at 90° at – 160225 kcal suggests it is more stable than either the 105° or 180° systems. The core-core repulsion energy indicates that the 90° system is less stable due to steric interactions. Both electronic and nuclear must be considered when predicting the lowest energy conformation in strained molecules.

BeH₂

Angle	Core-core Energy	Electronic Energy	Binding Energy	Orbital Energy					
				-4	-3	-2	-1	0	1
90	1188.87	-3030.88	-336.35	-20.81	-14.38	-0.01	2.27	7.42	8.91
95	1181.56	-3030.43	-343.21	-20.63	-14.77	0.09	2.27	7.59	8.72
100	1175.13	-3030.19	-349.39	-20.47	-15.14	0.20	2.26	7.76	8.52
105	1169.46	-3030.07	-354.96	-20.31	-15.47	0.31	2.26	7.93	8.31
110	1164.44	-3030.05	-359.95	-20.16	-15.78	0.43	2.25	8.09	8.09
115	1160.01	-3030.08	-364.40	-20.03	-16.06	0.56	2.25	7.86	8.24
120	1156.10	-3030.13	-368.37	-19.90	-16.32	0.70	2.24	7.63	8.39
125	1152.65	-3030.19	-371.88	-19.79	-16.56	0.84	2.24	7.39	8.53
130	1149.62	-3030.26	-374.98	-19.68	-16.77	1.00	2.23	7.15	8.67
135	1146.97	-3030.31	-377.68	-19.58	-16.96	1.15	2.23	6.90	8.79
140	1144.67	-3030.36	-380.03	-19.49	-17.13	1.31	2.22	6.67	8.90
145	1142.69	-3030.39	-382.04	-19.41	-17.28	1.47	2.22	6.44	9.00
150	1141.02	-3030.42	-383.74	-19.34	-17.41	1.62	2.22	6.22	9.08
155	1139.63	-3030.43	-385.14	-19.29	-17.52	1.77	2.21	6.01	9.16
160	1138.51	-3030.44	-386.27	-19.24	-17.61	1.91	2.21	5.83	9.22
165	1137.65	-3030.45	-387.14	-19.20	-17.68	2.03	2.21	5.67	9.27
170	1137.05	-3030.45	-387.75	-19.17	-17.73	2.13	2.21	5.55	9.30
175	1136.68	-3030.45	-388.11	-19.16	-17.76	2.18	2.21	5.48	9.32
180	1136.56	-3030.45	-388.23	-19.15	-17.77	2.21	2.21	5.45	9.33

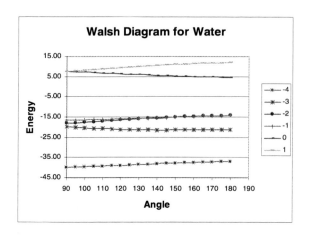

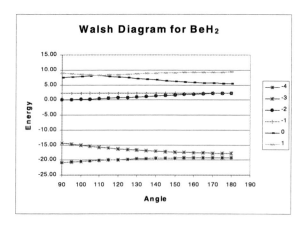

21. The Jahn-Teller Effect

Axial Length	MnF_6^{3-} Energy	NiF_6^{3-} Energy
1.50	450.5	-140.5
1.55	381.6	-135.6
1.60	324.7	-158.1
1.65	277.4	-173.2
1.70	239.1	-182.4
1.75	20.58	-187.2
1.80	179.8	-188.5
1.85	161.2	-186.9
1.90	148.5	-185.5
1.95	131.0	-185.1
2.00	111.4	-182.9
2.05	105.6	-179.2
2.10	85.2	-174.5
2.15	77.8	-169.0
2.20	73.5	-163.9
2.25	71.3	-156.7
2.30	70.7	-82.1
2.35	73.3	-81.9
2.40	75.	-81.5
2.45	92.7	-134.5
2.50	116.2	-80.9

25. The "Peptide Bond" in N-methylacetamide

Cis-trans Energy and Dipole Moment Differences

	OPLS (kcal/mol)	PM3 (kcal/mol)	Experiment (kcal/mol)	Dipole Moment (D)	Experiment Dipole Moment (D)
cis	3.897	-1109.8		4.21	
trans	0.532	-1101.3		4.04	
cis – trans			2.07	0.17	

Charge Distribution

	Carbonyl Carbon	Carbonyl Oxygen	Peptide Nitrogen
cis-	0.237	-0.371	-0.050
trans-	0.234	-0.365	-0.043

Geometric Information

	OPLS	PM3	Experimental
cis-bond lengths (Å)			
N-CH$_3$	1.451	1.471	1.445
N-CO	1.337	1.430	1.357
C=O	1.230	1.22	1.200
trans bond lengths (Å)			
N-CH$_3$	1.453	1.472	1.447
N-CO	1.343	1.429	1.353
C=O	1.229	1.222	1.200
cis-bond angles (°)			
H-N-CH$_3$	117.82	112.5	114.0
H-N-CO	119.18	114.4	127.4
trans- bond angles (°)			
H-N-CH$_3$	116.07	112.8	121.5
H-N-CO	117.28	113.1	119.4

27. The Inversion Barrier in Ammonia and Aniline

The Pyramidal and Planar Forms of Ammonia

Method	Pyramidal Energy (kcal/mol)	Planar Energy (kcal/mol)	Difference	Bond Angle (°)
ab initio	-35086.49	-35079.159	7.331	106.5
AM1	-276.632	-272.391	4.241	109.1
PM3	-272.407	-262.422	9.985	108.0

Aniline

Method	Pyramidal Structure (kcal/mol)	Planar Structure (kcal/mol)	Energy Difference
AM1 Energy (kcal/mol)	-1482.74	-1481.74	
H-N-H angle	113.09°		
C-N-H angle	114.18°		
PM3 Energy (kcal/mol)	-1481.94	-1777.47	
H-N-H angle	111.55°		
C-N-H angle	111.55°		

28. Heats of Formation of Conjugated Hydrocarbons

Compound	Structure	$\Delta_f H$ experimental (kcal/mol)	$\Delta_f H$ for PM3 optimized structure (kcal/mol)	$\Delta_f H$ for AM1 optimized structure (kcal/mol)
Ethylene		12.53	16.39	16.57
trans-Butadiene		26.00, 26.75	30.91	29.79
Benzene		19.82	23.29	21.87
Naphthalene		35.99, 36.25	40.42	40.35
Anthracene		55.17	61.32	62.61
Phenanthrene		48.09, 49.46	54.69	57.13
Pyrene		53.94	63.77	67.00
Toluene		11.95	13.91	14.22
o-Xylene		19.0	5.97	7.79
m-Xylene		17.2	4.56	6.62
p-Xylene		17.9	4.55	6.57
1-Methyl-2-ethyl benzene		0.29	5.56	6.58
1-Methyl-3-ethyl benzene		-0.46	0.99	1.29
1-Methyl-4-ethyl benzene		-0.78	0.97	1.23

29. Heat of Combustion of Fuels

Compound	$\Delta_f H$ AM1 (kcal/mol)	% Oxygen	$\Delta_{comb}H$ (kcal/mol)	$\Delta_{comb}H$ (kcal/gram)
"Kerosene" $C_{11}H_{24}$	-79.49	0	-1510.1	9.87
"Octane" n-C_8H_{18}	-58.86	0	-1113.4	9.77
"Iso-octane" 2,2,4-trimethylpentane	-46.99	0	-1125.24	9.87
Butanol, C_4H_9OH	-76.51	21.6	-615.75	8.32
Ethanol, C_2H_5OH	62.77	34.8	274.7	6.0
CO_2	-79.85			
H_2O	-59.27			

32. Intermolecular Hydrogen Bonding

Water-Formaldehyde

Δ_fH - Structure #1	-86.27 kcal/mol
Δ_fH - Structure #2	-89.31 kcal/mol
Δ_fH Water	-53.46 kcal/mol
Δ_fH Formaldehyde	-34.13 kcal/mol

Trifluoroethanol

The two possible modes of hydrogen bonding clearly show a difference in the O and the H charges on the atoms involved in the bridge.

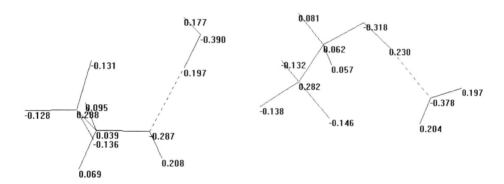

Base pairs

Students could use the bases in the Nucleic Acid database to facilitate this portion. Optimization of the structures is a time-consuming process even with a semi-empirical method!

33. Steric Energy of Cubanes

Compound	MM+ Energy (kcal/mol)	PM3 $\Delta_f H$ (kcal/mol)	$\Delta_{comb} H$ (kcal/mol)	$\Delta_{comb} H$ (kcal/gram)
Octane	4.74	-48.46		
Cubane	253.46	114.42		
Tetranitrocubane	258.32	131.74		
Octanitrocubane	287.23	208.75		
Trinitrotoluene	19.36	11090		
Carbon Dioxide	0	-84.12		
Water	0	-53.13		

34. Tautomerism of 7-Aminopyrazolopyrimidine

Energies in kcal/mol

	ΔH Neutral Form (kcal/mol)	ΔH N1-Protonated Form (kcal/mol)	ΔH N3 Protonated Form (kcal/mol)
N7H	106.35	256.32	250.40
N8H	107.79	249.57	245.87
$\Delta(\Delta H)$ N7H-N8H	-1.44	6.78	4.53

35. Resonance Energy: Benzene and Hexasilabenzene

Compound	$\Delta_f H$ (kcal/mol)	Silicon Analog	$\Delta_f H$ (kcal/mol)
Benzene C_6H_6	21.88	Si_6H_6	144.68
Cyclohexane C_6H_{12}	-38.78	Si_6H_{12}	50.22
Cyclododecatriene $C_{12}H_{18}$	18.38	$Si_{12}H_{18}$	196.82
ΔU			

Hexasilabenzene Isomers

Isomer	AM1 Binding energy (kcal/mol)
1. Hexasilbenzene (D_{6h}),	-818.5
2. Hexasilaprismane (D_{3h}),	-849.3
3. Hexasila-Dewar benzene (C_{2v})	-820.7
4. tris-(disilanediyl)	-729.7

Sax *et al.* concluded that isomer #2 lies 41 kJ/mol (9.7 kcal/mol) below #1 and at least 100 kJ/mol (23.9 kcal/mol) below #3.   They also found that #1 was not planar but adopts a chairlike puckered structure that is about 7 kJ/mol (1.7 kcal/mol) more stable than the planar structure with torsions about 16-18 degrees.   Isomer #4 was over 200 kJ/mol (47.8 kcal/mol) higher than #2.

36. Flavin Redox Chemistry

Isomer Number	C$_7$	C$_8$	C$_9$	E° at pH 7.4 (mV)	AM1 LUMO (eV)
9	H	H	H	-407	-1.715
10	CH$_3$	H	H	-419	-1.679
11	H	CH$_3$	H	-439	-1.682
12	CH$_3$	CH$_3$	H	-456	-1.649
22	OCH$_3$	H	H	-396	-1.741
23	H	N(CH$_3$)$_3$	H	-580	-1.406
26	H	H	CH$_3$	-357	-1.680
27	CH$_3$	H	CH$_3$	-370	-1.643
28	H	CH$_3$	CH$_3$	-368	-1.638

The results need to be sorted prior to graphing. The graph below was produced with Excel. Notice that a fairly linear relationship is seen for compounds 9-23. For compounds 26-28 where the substitution occurs at the carbon adjacent to N10, distortion of the ring occurs in the optimized geometry, the trend does not hold.

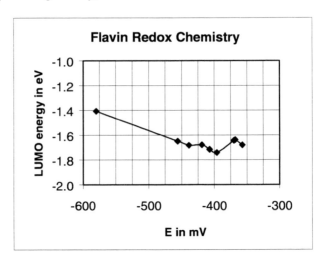

37. Permanent Dipole Moments

	PM3 (D)	CNDO (D)	AM1 (D)	Experiment (D)
HCl	1.38	2.04	1.38	1.08
Chlorobenzene	0.95	2.89	1.31	1.69
Acetonitrile	3.21	3.18	2.89	3.92
Dimethyl ether	1.26	1.91	1.43	1.30
Method rms deviation[*]	0.08	0.91	0.56	

[*]Method root mean square deviation is $\sqrt{(\sum d_i^2 / n)}$

	Angle (°)	Vector Addition Method (D)	Quantum Mechanical Calculation (D)	Experimental (D)
o-Dichlorobenzene	60		1.35	2.50
m-Dichlorobenzene	120		0.88	1.72
Chloromethane			1.38	1.87
Dichloromethane	109.5		1.36	1.60

Molecule	Vector Addition Method (D)	PM3 Calculation (D)	Experimental Result (D)
Dimethyl ether		1.26	1.30
Diethyl ether	(same as above)	1.29	1.20
THF	(nearly same as above)	1.64	1.60

38. Dipole moment of Flexible Molecules

Experimental Data

	PM3 Energy (kcal/mol)	PM3 Dipole Moment (D)
CH_3CN	-587.87	3.21
Gauche-succinonitrile	-1059.27	2.75
Trans-succinonitrile	-1057.06	5.38

Calculated Results

	Experiment	Calculated
$\Delta E = E(\text{gauche}) - E(\text{trans})$		-2.21 kcal/mol
X_{trans}		0.333
$<\mu^2>$		18.3 D^2
$<\mu>$ in toluene	2.97(-90°C) to 3.93(+90°C)	4.28 D

39. The Effect of Dielectric Medium on Rotational State

	Bond Dipole Method		Atomic Charge Method $\varepsilon = 1$		Atomic Charge Method $\varepsilon = 4$	
	μ (D)	Energy (kcal/mol)	μ (D)	Energy (kcal/mol)	μ (D)	Energy (kcal/mol)
Trans	0.024	4.50	0.002	-0.879	0.001	-1.23
Gauche	3.81	8.61	0.320	2.75	0.280	2.93

40. Charge Transfer and Excited State Dipole Moments

Molecule and μ_{ground}	Transition Occup MO → Unocc. MO	λ (nm)	Oscillator Strength	$\mu_{excited}$	$\Delta\mu = \mu_{ex} - \mu_{gr}$
Aniline					
μ_{ground} = 1.365	18 → 19	190.1	0.855	3.037	
	17 → 19	187.5	0.962	2.258	
p-Nitroaniline					
μ_{ground} = 7.748	26 → 27	329.8	0.428	22.162	
	24 → 27	211.1	0.216	5.357	
	26 → 28	187.2	1.246	8.318	
	26 → 27	185.6	0.976	8.078	
m-Nitroaniline					
μ_{ground} =6.652	25 → 27	288.7	0.210	18.173	
	26 → 29	228.8	0.292	9.128	
	24 → 27	210.8	0.317	3.873	
	26 → 28	186.6	0.858	6.883	
	24 → 27	183.9	1.148	6.590	
p-Nitromethoxy benzene					
μ_{ground} = 6.105	29 → 30	307.3	0.374	19.512	
	29 → 31	184.6	1.363	6.354	
	28 → 31	184.1	1.052	6.450	

m-Nitromethoxy benzene					
μ_{ground} = 7.360	28 → 30	286.9	0.290	19.470	
	27 → 30	210.3	0.341	5.393	
	28 → 32	184.4	0.964	7.425	
p-Nitrophenyl acetylene					
μ_{ground} = 6.230	27 → 28	320.0	0.575	22.691	
	27 → 29	229.8	0.315	11.416	
	27 → 30	196.3	0.727	6.296	
m-Nitrophenyl acetylene					
μ_{ground} = 5.814	26 → 28	283.6	0.257	18.092	
	27 → 29	241.1	0.820	8.054	
	26 → 30	187.0	0.653	6.413	

41. UV Spectra of Polycyclic Aromatic Hydrocarbons

Molecule	β (intense peak) $\varepsilon \cong 1\text{-}2$	p (weaker, non-zero peak) $\varepsilon \cong .1$	α (forbidden, zero intensity) $\varepsilon = 0$
Naphthalene	229	338	342
Anthracene	253	402	300,364
Tetracene	272	460	345,375
Pentacene	286	510	377,388
Phenanthrene	258	349	344

42. Vibrational Spectra

Molecule	PM3 Frequency (cm^{-1})	PM3 Oscillator Strength	Experimental Frequency(cm^{-1})
Alkenes C=C stretch			
Cyclohexene	1878	0.094	1646
Cyclopentene	1829	0.030	1611
Cyclobutene	1774	0.002	1566
Cyclopropene	1925	0.303	1641
Acetylene	2138	0.000	1974
Cyclic ketones C=O stretch			
Cyclohexanone	1985	99.208	1715
Cyclopentanone	2009	105.820	1740
Cyclobutanone	2077	129.585	1782
Cyclopropanone	2197	159.551	1822

43. The Spectra of Visual Pigments

Warning: Optimizing these structures in PM3 takes considerable time! This might be a good class project.

Molecule	PM3 λ_{max} (nm)	Oscillator Strength	Experimental λ_{max} (nm)	Extinction Coefficient ε (M^{-1}cm^{-1})
all-trans retinal	347.4	1.34		
11-cis retinal	348.5	1.25		
trans rhodopsin model	493.9	1.50	380	
11-cis rhodopsin model	501.2	1.29	500	40,000
all-trans vitamin A	341.3	1.25		
11-cis vitamin A	343.2	1.14		

Point Charge Position relative to 11-cis-retinal Schiff Base	λ_{max} (nm)
11-cis rhodopsin model from above	501.2
One about 10 Å from N$^+$	667.6
One about 10 Å from ring C=C	692.0
One near N$^+$ and one near ring C=C	595.6

44. Solvent Effects on Spectra

$n \rightarrow \pi^*$	Transition energy (nm)		Transition energy (cm^{-1})	
	$S \rightarrow T$	$S \rightarrow S$	$S \rightarrow T$	$S \rightarrow S$
Gas	419.21	368.16	23854	27162
Water	389.02	364.01	25706	27472
Acetonitrile	410.95	361.55	24334	27659
Chloroform	416.78	365.83	23993	27335

Shifts relative to gas phase

	Shift in cm^{-1}	
	$S \rightarrow T$	$S \rightarrow S$
Gas	0	
Water	-1852	-310
Acetonitrile	-480	-497
Chloroform	-139	-173

46. Stability of Carbocations

Dissociation Times in ps

	500K	1000K	1500K	2000K
1-Butanol	no	no	no	no
2-Butanol	no	0.50	0.29	0.21
tert-Butanol	0.20	0.069	0.045	0.036

Heat of Reaction

	$\Delta_f H$ of alcohol (kcal/mol)	$\Delta_f H$ of proton (kcal/mol)	$\Delta_f H$ of the C^+ ion (kcal/mol)	$\Delta_f H$ of water (kcal/mol)	$\Delta_{rxn} H$
1-butanol	-67.77	367.20	213.63	68.38	-17.42
2-butanol	-68.65	367.20	190.64	68.38	-39.53
tert-butanol	-71.46	367.20	178.60	68.38	-48.76

Spreadsheet Results

Cation Calculations	Total Energy	Total Energy	Total Energy
Bond Length (Å)	Primary (kcal/mol)	Secondary (kcal/mol)	Tertiary (kcal/mol)
1.00	-21260.2	-21262.4	-21261.4
1.25	-21407.1	-21411.6	-21413.6
1.50	-21432.4	-21439.0	-21444.2
1.75	-21428.0	-21437.4	-21445.1
2.00	-21421.1	-21433.4	-21443.8
2.25	-21416.4	-21432.9	-21444.4
2.50	-21420.3	-21436.0	-21446.2
2.75	-21422.0	-21437.0	-21447.1
3.00	-21421.4	-21436.9	-21447.3

48. Simulated Annealing

Trifluoromethyl simulation showing the two named torsions is shown. The authors of the paper found that the –OH points toward the -CF_3 group and the H-F distance was about 1.98Å. The –OH group was reported to be "slightly rotated" and the C-F involved in the hydrogen bond "considerably rotated" out of the plane of the ring.

They used phenol and trifluoromethyl benzene for comparing the other geometry features.

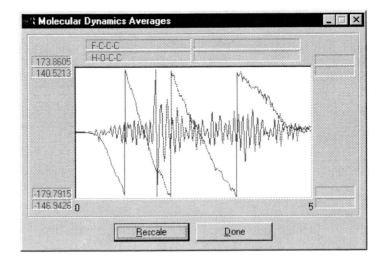

49. Langevin Dynamics

These are typical runs at the setting suggested in the experiment. Note that the oscillation is considerably damped using Langevin Dynamics although approximately the same range of values is observed for the torsion.

Molecular Dynamics

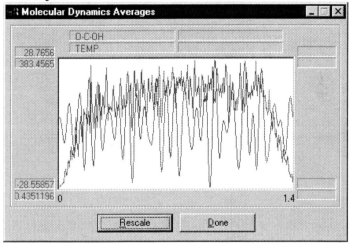

Langevin Dynamics

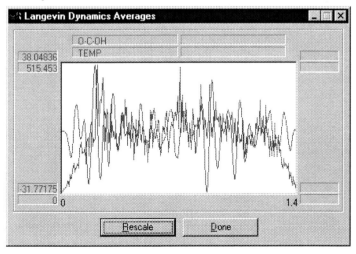

50. Intramolecular Vibrations

These typical simulation results were obtained for the fluorine and the bromine compounds. The harmonic changes in amplitude are evident only for the fluorine compound. If one observes the animation of vibrations using the Compute-Vibrations instead of the dynamics simulation, two strong bands are observed in the $1400\text{-}1500$ cm^{-1} region for the fluoride while only one intense band is observed for the other: 835 cm^{-1} for the chloride, 666 cm^{-1} for bromide and 660 cm^{-1} for the iodide.

Methyl Fluoride

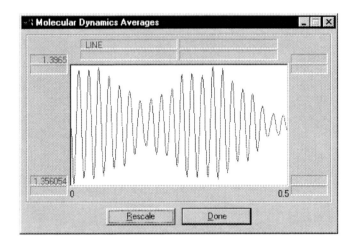

Methyl Bromide

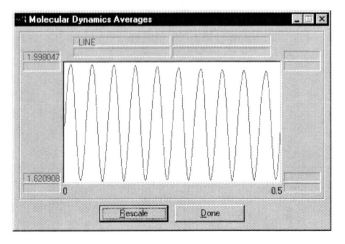

Vibration Frequency and Mass

	Experimental Frequency (cm^{-1})	Oscillations per 0.5 ps	Average distance (Å)
CH$_3$F	1400-1000	21	1.377
CH$_3$Cl	800-600	12.5	1.7851
CH$_3$Br	600-500	10	1.911
CH$_3$I	~500	9.5	2.055

Temperature Data for HBr

Beyond about 3000K, the number of oscillations changes and the amplitude decreases.

Temperature	Oscillations per 0.1 ps	Range High Value (Å)	Range Low Value (Å)	Amplitude Change
100	7.25	1.485	1.361	.0.124
300	7.25	1.512	1.338	0.174
500	7.25	1.540	1.315	0.225
800	7.25	1.573	1.289	0.284
1000	7.25	1.593	1.275	0.318
2000	7.25	1.670	1.224	0.446
000	7.1	1.635	1.299	0.336